my
lawnmower
hates me

The Only Good Lawnmower Is A Dead One

my lawnmower hates me

an original manual for
hand and power mowers

written by tom cuthbertson
illustrated by rick morrall

TEN SPEED PRESS

My Lawnmower Hates Me
is published by Ten Speed Press,
Box 4310, Berkeley, California 94704.
Single copies prepaid may be ordered from
the publisher: $3.95 paperback + 30c postage & handling,
$7.95 clothbound + 60c postage & handling.

ISBN 0-913668-13-3 paperback
ISBN 0-913668-14-1 clothbound
Library of Congress Catalog No. 73-77727
Beverly Anderson Graphic Design, San Francisco
Printed in The United States of America

*This book
is dedicated to
Archie Bunker*

ACKNOWLEDGMENTS

Loving thanks to Pat.
And to those others who
taught me how to relate
to damn old lawnmowers:
Dick Kenville,
C. G. Robb,
Clyde McGuire,
William Carter,
Gary Mcdonald,
Karen Swanner and
    friend, Howard.

Contents

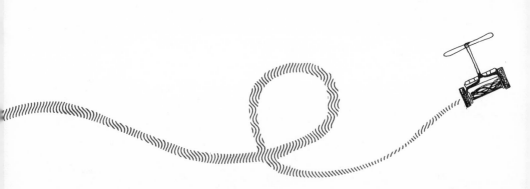

Introduction

UMANIZING a hated machine; that's what this book is for. We have all thought, at one time or another, that our lawnmowers are out to get us. The goddamn things either won't start, or won't stop, or won't cooperate and cut the lawn instead of the petunias or the sprinkler heads or our own toes. Mowers can be more than stubborn or willful: they can get downright *vicious*.

But they can be pretty compatible, if you just learn the procedures for relating to them. A mower is not all that complicated a machine. It's simple enough that you can learn which parts need to be respected for their vicious tendencies (like the BLADES, for instance), and which parts have to be attended to now and then (like the spark plug and air cleaner on a power mower). The procedures for respectfully attending the parts of your mower are all in this book, and if you follow them carefully, you can do them with ease.

There's no reason why you should have to load your mower into the back of the car (a pain in the neck in itself) at least once a year, and have some sniggering mechanic tell you it may be six weeks before you can mow down the elephant grass in your front yard so you can get up the walk to the door. Why should you wait? You can fix the bugger yourself! What's better, you can learn to keep the mower running well, so it won't give you any hassles. Just remember the RULES-OF-THUMB below, and do the annual spring and fall check-ups (see

1

Appendices) and you won't have to take the mower to the shop for a long time.

You might learn to relate to your mower quite well even if you never manage to enjoy the job of mowing the lawn. It will be enough of an accomplishment if there is one less machine that you are enslaved to; if *you* can learn to push your *mower* around, instead of having *it* bug *you*.

If you learn to be the boss over a power mower, you will also learn a great deal about gas engines, so that hopefully, you might get one step closer to understanding that other gas-powered machine that gives us so much trouble, the Automobile.

If you develop a decent relationship with your Hand Mower, who knows, you might even get so you can enjoy such simple pleasures as the sound of a perfectly adjusted mower whirring and clicking, and the smell of a smogless, fresh-cut lawn on a warm spring day.

Rules-of-Thumb

1. All through this book, the term "left side" means the left side of the mower as it faces forward. "Right side" means right on the mower facing forward too.

2. On most bolts and nuts, clockwise (abbreviated cl in this book) tightens, and counter-clockwise (abbreviated c-cl) loosens. If the procedure tells you to tighten something to a number of foot-pounds, use a Torque Wrench (See Tools appendix) and tighten (cl) to the right number.

3. Any two parts that screw together have threads. And threads are easy to strip. To avoid stripped threads, first make sure both parts have the same threads, then start screwing them together slowly and carefully. Never force two threaded parts to screw together if they resist. And don't tighten bolts and nuts too tight. Remember that the smaller the bolt or nut, the gentler you have to be. When tightening tiny screws that hold covers on, take it easy.

4. Nine-tenths of the work you do to solve any mechanical problem goes to finding out just where the problem is. If you have a problem and you know generally where it is, before you start dismantling random parts of the mower, use the DESCRIPTION sections in this book to help you get oriented and find the specific trouble.

5. Dismantle as little as possible to do any repair. When you do have to take something apart, take it apart slowly. The more time you spend learning the order of a unit's parts as you dismantle it, the less time you will spend reassembling the unit correctly. Lay the little parts out in a row, in the order they come off. That'll make it super easy.

6. Don't read this book without looking at your mower. This is a three-way conversation among you, your lawnmower, and this book; don't leave anybody out. Step by step, do it together.

7. Think a minute before you attack rust-frozen bolts and nuts. Is there any way you can get by without loosening that bolt or nut? Are you going to be able to replace the parts around the frozen bolt or nut if you do ruin them with your violent efforts? If not, proceed with great caution.

Try Liquid Wrench or some other penetrating oil (you can get it at auto parts stores) before you use any tools. After you squirt it on, let it soak in for a few minutes, and give the stuck part a few *light* taps with a hammer to encourage the oil on its way. When you are ready to use wrenches and screwdrivers, use only ones that fit well. If no amount of wrenching and screwing will get the parts loose, first make sure they don't loosen clockwise (cl) instead of the normal counter-clockwise (c-cl), then resort to the good old hacksaw and cut the bolt off. When you finally get the parts loosened or sawed apart, promise yourself that you won't leave the poor old mower out in the weather again. Ever.

8. Use your head. If your mower has some part that's slightly different from those described in the book, think for a minute about the differences, and proceed with them in mind. Don't let your mower's idiosyncracies throw you off, just treat them with due respect.

9. Find a mower shop that *cares*. It may not be the big fancy shop; it'll be the shop with the people who are helpful. There are people like that in some shops. When you find a good shop, do all your business there, and send your friends there to buy mowers. Be kind to the shop that is decent to you, and it will help you when this book can't.

10. Cultivate a fine ear so you can hear any little complaint your mower is making, like grindy bearings, or blades clacking against the cutter bar, or an engine chugging and missing for want of air or gas. You don't have to talk to the mower, just learn to listen respectfully for its warning sounds of trouble.

Illustration 1
Lawnmower Overkill

Chapter 1
Which Mower for You?

Take a good look at the thickness of your wallet, the size of your lawn, and the extent of your willpower before you go down to the lawnmower shop to look at all the latest gadgety models.

   Don't spend more than you have to on any mower. It's possible, nowadays, to spend about $1,300 on a contraption they *call* a lawnmower (it's actually a customized tractor with a rotary mower under it; see illustration 1). That's utter idiocy, unless your lawn is a golf course. I mean, for that price, you could buy a hand mower and pay one of the neighbor's kids to push it around your lawn every Saturday for a couple of years! Don't, on the other hand, try so hard to save money on a mower that you have to fight with a piece of junk every Saturday morning, and spend weeks waiting for parts. It costs a little more to buy from a mower shop rather than from a discount house or department store, but then you don't have to send the mower to outer Cucamonga for two months when it needs professional attention.

Buy a mower that's suited for the kind of work you need to do with it. For instance, if you have a postage stamp size lawn, or even two little lawns, one in front of the house and one in back, which add up to less than 3,000 square feet (60 feet by 50 feet), get a good, solid hand mower. It will be comparatively light and maneuverable for the confined area of your lawn, easy to store in a small space, and much less demanding of maintenance than any power mower (see illustration 2). You will have to push it, but it will be less work than a big cranky power mower with all of its maintenance, starting, and storage hassles. Besides, a hand mower can be really very quiet and relaxing to use, if it's given a little attention now and then.

If you have more than an eighth of an acre (roughly 5,000 square feet, or a 100 foot by 50 foot plot) of lawn, maintaining a power mower will be less work than shoving a hand mower around and around all the time. Among the different power mowers, the basic, reasonable choices can be narrowed down to three: the gas-powered reel type, the gas-powered rotary, and the electric rotary.

The gas-powered reel type mower is ideal for a hardy, big, simply shaped lawn with *gently* sloping or dipping

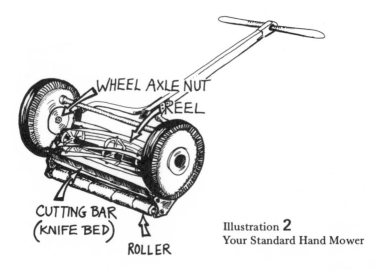

Illustration 2
Your Standard Hand Mower

surfaces, but good flush decks or header boards all the way around. It does best with a meticulous owner who likes to mow often and keep the grass quite short, even if this means spending a bit more money to buy the mower, and spending more time to keep it in perfect adjustment (see illustration 3). The meticulous owner will be well rewarded for his investment of time and money. His lawn will look like a beautiful carpet, even if he mows it when it's still damp with morning dew.

The gas-powered rotary mower is built for a big flat lawn with irregular edges around trees, gardens, and walls. The owner should be one who doesn't care if the grass is only cut down to 1½ inches tall instead of half an inch like a putting green. If this owner happens to get lazy and let the grass grow to several inches high, that's OK by the rotary mower too; in fact, even weeds can be mowed down with it, as long as they aren't wet. The rotary mower will do lots of tough work without much complaint or maintenance, if it's a sturdy, simple model without any complicated attachment gismos. It will require a larger storage area than any of the other mowers, but it will also require a smaller outlay of cash than any other mower of similar quality. This is why it's so popular.

The electric rotary mower is suited for cutting small, obstacle-free lawns that are near electrical outlets. If the lawn owner is the type who would rather spend his time working with a quiet, light machine that takes longer and has to be kept untangled, rather than a fast, heavy, noisy mower, then he should try an electric. The cost is roughly comparable to that of the gas-powered mower, but the lower speed of the rotary blade on an electric does mean that you get less cutting power for your money than you can with a smoggy old gas-powered rotary. Electric mowers can't be asked to do tough work, like mowing weeds. They burn up under loads; if an electric mower dies from an overload, it's dead for good. A gas mower that dies can be started up again most of the time.

Each of the three power mower types, when used in

the situation for which it is ideal, requires a minimum of work; the self-powered reel mower will chug up and down slopes, the rotary will move in and out of awkward lawn edges and over high grass, and the light electric will glide easily over a small, trim lawn.

But between the three ideal situations for the three mower types, there are endless shades of gray. If, for instance, you have a big, hilly lawn with irregular edges, you'll have to either hassle with pushing the rotary mower up and down the hills (that can be *very* dangerous—see Appendix, *Appendages*), or hassle with getting a self-powered reel type mower in and out of the tricky corners without digging its wheels into the turf. I'd rather have a mower that only goes when I want it to. Never trusted them willful self-powered buggers. You might like controlling the will of a reel lawnmower, though. You might even be tempted by a self-powered rotary job; they are a poor

Illustration **3**
The Ups and Downs of a Power Reel Mower

compromise between the two basic mowers, though, and something to be avoided simply because of their enormous weight (90 pounds plus) if for no other reason.

The complicated and precise power reel mowers with big wide drive wheels in back and the reel and catcher up front should be left to professional gardeners or real mechanic types. They require more finicky adjustments than I can cover in this book. "Rider" mowers (see illustration) look like a lazy man's dream, but they require an auto mechanic for repairs. They are also hard on lawns and *very* dangerous, so leave them alone.

Whichever type of mower you decide you want, hand or power, read the introduction to the chapter on that type before you pick out a particular brand or model. Also, if you're about to get a power mower, read the introduction to the Engine chapter carefully, and follow the hints given.

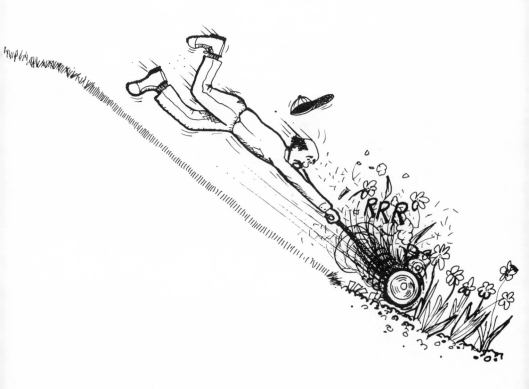

Your Standard
Hand Mower

Shopping Hints

A hand mower can be much less work than a power mower, if you don't have too much lawn to cover, and if you do the mowing frequently enough that the grass never gets too high.

Any good hand mower will require less maintenance than its powered cousins, but when you are looking for a new or used hand mower, do get as good a one as you can afford. How do you check for quality? Easy.

Check the basic running gear first. Does the mower you are looking at have two-wheel drive? Tip the mower back on its roller (see illustration 2) and turn each wheel in the direction it turns as you push the mower. Do both wheels spin the blades? (WATCH your fingers—them blades just love to mow pinkies down to ½ inch!) While you have the mower tipped up on its roller, get your head down close to the blades, (not *too* close, now) and find the cutter bar, the heavy bar that runs from one side of the mower frame to the other down at the bottom; the bar should be almost brushed by the passing reel blades. Those blades missing by a mile? Or whacking against the bar now and then? Or missing at one end, and hitting at the other? If the reel blades are whacking the cutter bar at irregular intervals, or if the bar is bowed or bent in such a way that the space between it and the blades changes, then the lawnmower will never work without major repairs. If the blades and the cutter bar are simply too close or too far from each other, turn the mower right side up again and see whether there are cutter bar adjusting bolts or nuts on the side-plates of the frame of the mower. These are always near the backs of the side-plates, but there are several different types (see illustration 8a, b, c, d, e for examples). If a mower you are considering has these bolts and (on old mowers) they aren't rusted into place, then you can adjust the cutter bar.

If an old mower has adjusting bolts and they seem to be operable, check to make sure they aren't set all the way to one extreme. Look closely at the tips of the adjusting bolts. If one is screwed all the way in almost, and the other one is screwed all the way out so that its tip is hidden from view by the arm that sticks up from the cutter bar and the nub of the side-plate, you're looking at a mower that has been sharpened so many times that the blades are worn away to the point that the cutter bar can't be adjusted to come close to them (see illustration 8a). Pass up the mower and look for one with less mileage on it.

On some newer mowers, the cutter bar adjusting bolts are on the outside of the mower frame. This makes for easier adjustment, and keeps your fingers away from those hungry reel blades.

Check the thickness and solidness of the frame side-plates that the adjusting bolts are attached to on any mower. The frame should be of thick, heavy steel, not thin, tinny, stamped out pieces of metal. Not only do you want a strong mower that won't bend, you want a mower that's heavy enough to cut right through thick grass, instead of "floating up" and riding over it.

Take a look at the roller. On an old mower, a bent or decayed roller will be hard to replace. On any new mower, the best kind of roller is the high-impact rubberized plastic type. Good hardwood is rarely used anymore, so a wood roller on a new mower can be expected to decay rapidly, as can a soft rubber one.

Grab the handle and try to twist it. It should be made of sturdy enough material that it won't bend or break with heavy use. On old mowers, the wooden parts of the handle can be replaced, but the pieces often have to be specially made; they can wind up costing more than another whole mower.

Finally, push a prospective mower and back it up a few times. If it's new, it should roll easily, without the blades hitting enough to slow it down. Ask if the reel bearings are of oil-impregnated brass. That kind of bearing doesn't need lubrication. On an old mower, the bearings will not be oil-impregnated, and may well need oil or adjustment, or even replacement. Stop the mower and hold it still with one hand on the brush bar. Then grasp the reel firmly, being careful not to cut yourself on its sharp blades, and see if it can wiggle around on its bearings. If it can, the mower needs major adjustments or, more likely, a complete overhaul and replacement of the bearings. Not worth the hassle. Find another mower with tight bearings. Does the mower work, but noisily and roughly, especially when you pull it backwards? That's OK. It probably just needs cleaning and lubrication.

If a mower passes all the above inspections, there are several frills or extra pluses to look for. Are the wheels bigger than 9 inches in diameter? If so, great. Bigger than 10 inches is that much better. How wide is the reel from one end of the blades to the other? 16 inches is OK. 18 inches is best. Rare 20 inch wide mowers can be awkward for a small person or an intricately shaped lawn. How many blades on the reel? 4 is minimal, 5 is great, 6 is rare and very good for making a close-clipped, smooth-looking lawn.

On some fancy newer mowers, there are levers and knobs that do various things. A reverse lever, which will allow you to put the reel in reverse motion by backing the wheels up, makes blade sharpening quick, safe, and easy. But this lever is rarely seen. More common is a lever or knob for adjusting the wheel position, so you can cut the lawn to any height from ½ inch to 2 inches. This gismo strikes me as superfluous for anything but a very specialized lawn, or weed cutting. To use it you always have to remember to adjust the roller as well as the wheel position, which is a bother. So unless you have a dichondra, manicured super-lawn, or recurrent weed problems, I'd forget the cutting height adjuster.

On the issue of grass catchers, there are two schools of thought. People in one school mow their lawns often. The clippings are therefore quite small, and aren't collected, but rather allowed to sink down into the lawn, decay, and act as fertilizer. The second school doesn't mow so often, and therefore has to collect the grass clippings. Long clippings, left in large amounts, will form a tight mat over a lawn, especially in dry seasons when clippings don't decay quickly. The mat or thatch sheds water off the lawn, blocks air from getting to the soil, and generally works to ruin the grass plants. If you are going to join the second school, and will need a grass catcher, check any mower you're looking at to make sure there are brackets near the ends of the roller for the grass catcher.

Hand Mower Wheels

Description
You know, the round things on the sides of the mower with rubber tires on them (usually). Working from the outside in, they are made up of a hub cap (which is often missing), the metal body of the wheel and the tire, a row of teeth inside the rim, and a bearing surface, often of oil-impregnated bronze, which turns on an axle. The wheel is held on the axle either by a cotter pin or "C" ring that's stuck on the end of the axle, or a bolt that runs through the center of the axle.

A small gear, the pinion gear, is turned by the teeth on the inside of the wheel rim. The pinion gear and a pawl inside it spin the axle of the mower's reel rapidly when the wheel goes forward; the pawl in the axle disengages and lets the reel coast when the wheel is turned backwards (see illustration 4).

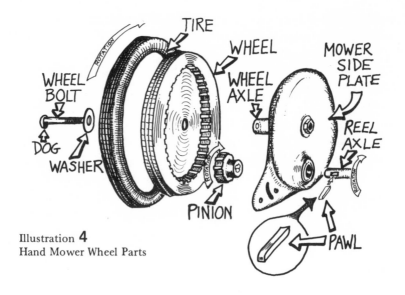

Illustration **4**
Hand Mower Wheel Parts

On mowers with adjustable cutting height, the whole wheel assembly is attached to a separate plate from the side-plate of the mower. The wheel plate pivots around the reel axle and, on some models, is moved either by a lever or a thumb screw attachment mounted on an extra brush bar; on more primitive adjustable-height models, the wheel assembly can be taken out of its axle hole in the mower side-plate, and moved to a higher or lower axle hole.

Problems

WHEELS WON'T TURN
The problem could be with the reel blades, or with the wheels, or both. To locate the problem, pull the mower backwards. Do the wheels turn easily in reverse? If they do, and make a nice clicking noise as they roll, then the problem is with the reel, not the wheels. See Reel Problems, *Reel Hitting Bar.* If the wheels make terrible noises in reverse, or if they don't roll backwards, or if they turn the reel backwards, or even if they roll backwards without

making any hint of a clicking noise, then something is kaput or in need of attention in the works of the wheel. It's time for a

WHEEL OVERHAUL

Overhaul one wheel at a time to keep things simple. Start by putting the mower on a clean smooth surface, like a cement patio or garage floor. *Not* out on the lawn, where you will lose small parts and find them later, jammed in your mower blades. Grab the brush bar and tip the mower back on its roller until the handle rests on the floor (see illustration 2; power mower people, look at illustration 22 instead). Take the hubcap off one wheel, if your mower is snazzy enough to have hubcaps. To get the cap off, stick the end of a thin-bladed screwdriver under an edge and twist. If the cap is persistent, stick the screwdriver blade under the cap on the opposite side and twist again. If the cap is held on by screws, you obviously can't pry it off. Unscrew (c-cl) the screws and take the cap off. Look at the middle of the hubcapless wheel to see what holds it on.

If there is the end of a shaft sticking out there with a cotter pin through it (a cotter pin is a wire thing that looks like a miniature bobby pin, with the ends bent around the shaft), all you have to do is bend the ends of the pin out straight and squeeze them together with a pair of pliers, then pull the pin out. Instead of a cotter pin, your wheel may have a "C" ring holding it on. The "C" ring will be in a slot that runs around the end of the axle shaft. To remove the ring, push the points of the "C" with the points of a needle-nose pliers. Hold onto the back of the "C" as it spreads and comes off—otherwise it'll shoot away where you can't find it. Put the cotter pin or "C" ring in a safe place, like in a dixie cup, and slide the wheel off the axle.

More often, there is the smooth head of a bolt or rivet in the middle of the wheel, instead of a cotter pin or "C" ring (see illustration 4). For these models you have to do some research before you can try to get the wheel off. Think of a straight line going through the wheel horizontally, from the smooth bolt or rivet head toward the middle of the mower. Now look on the inside of the sideplate of the mower where your imaginary line would emerge. Is there a nut on the end of a bolt there? If so, good. You have a decent mower. If not, there will probably be the flared-out end of a rivet there, which means your mower is a bugger to overhaul. You have to just get oil or grease into the gears behind the wheel however you can, and hope for the best. But let's assume you have a neato mower with a bolted-on wheel. You can get the nut loose (c-cl) with a wrench. Hold the mower still by the brush bar as you start to loosen (c-cl) the nut, then just push the head of the bolt (in the middle of the outside of the wheel) with a finger as you continue to undo (c-cl) the loose nut with the other hand. The thing that keeps the bolt from turning is either a metal tooth (called a dog) or a square shoulder under the round bolt head. There is a corresponding hole for the dog or square shoulder in the end of the axle, so if you push the bolt head, it'll stay put instead of turning. (If the bolt spins even when you hold its head in, the dog or shoulder is screwed up—saw off the damn bolt at the nut end with a hacksaw and make a mental note to get a replacement.) When the nut comes off, pull the bolt out, then take it and any washers that were around it and put them all back together and in a dixie cup so they won't get confused with other parts, or lost.

After you have removed the cotter pin, "C" ring, or bolt that was holding your wheel on, grab the brush bar again and hold the mower still as you wiggle the wheel off its bearings. DON'T turn the wheel back and forth as you try to wriggle it free. You might give the reel blades a whirl and shave the hair and some of the skin off your knuckles. As the wheel comes off, it may bring along the pinion, a short fat cylinder that has gear teeth running around it. If the pinion does fall out on the floor, watch for a little flat metal pin, the pawl. The pawl will be in a slot in the reel axle to start with; it is held in that slot by the pinion normally. But with the pinion gone, the pawl may just slide out of its slot and follow the pinion to the floor. Find it and put it with the pinion in a safe place, like a dixie cup. Take a quick look at the pinion to see if there is some mark on it, like an "L" or an "R" stamped in the metal somewhere. No mark? Well, get your marking pen out and make one, "L" if it is the pinion from the left wheel, facing forward as the mower goes, "R" if it's the other.

You may have a kind of mower which doesn't let the pinion and pawl fall off when the wheel is gone. Your pinion will be held on by a "C" ring. To get the "C" ring out of its slot, push the points of the "C" with the points of needle-nose pliers. The opening of the "C" will spread and slip in the slot around the reel axle. Put your hand around the "C" when it gets near to coming off, or it'll shoot across the cement floor in search of some lawn to get lost in. In addition to the "C" ring, this type of mower will have a washer behind the pinion—don't let it get away from you either.

Examine the wheel parts, whichever type of wheel you have dismantled. Are they rusty and dry? Or oily, but gummed up with dirt and lawn clippings? Clean them as needed with your wire parts brush and some solvent or gas. Get all the rusty scale or gunk and clippings. Make sure the teeth of the wheel and pinion are unclogged, and get all sticky stuff off the pawl and out of the pawl's slot in the reel axle. Now look closely at the pinion teeth. Are they worn or chipped badly? They wear down much more quickly than the wheel gear teeth, so if they are OK, you can figure the wheel teeth are fine, unless one has chipped off. Even if the pinion teeth are OK, the pinion might have another common ailment. Turn it on end, with the small hole down, and look closely at the ratchet slots in the big hole. If they look like the worn-down ones in illustration 5, the pinion is shot. Look at the pawl now. Is it broken or missing altogether, or worn beyond recognition?

GOOD PINION RATCHET

GOOD TEETH

WORN PINION RATCHET

WORN & CHIPPED TEETH

Illustration **5**
Good and Bad Pinions

If either the pawl or the pinion is worn, chipped, or damaged, go *with them in hand* to get exact replacements from your local mower repair shop. Make sure you get a pinion that is the same size and for the same wheel. The pawl can look slightly different from the original, but it must be the same length and width. If you replace both parts with the correct size new ones, you'll be sure to get a good fit.

When you have clean usable or nice shiny new pinions and pawls, get out some lithium-base grease and glob a bunch of it around the pinion teeth and in the ratchet grooves. Put some more in the reel axle slot where the pawl goes. You don't have to go to the trouble of filling in all the wheel gear teeth with grease—the pinion will spread its ample supply around on them.

Start reconstruction of the wheel by turning the reel axle by hand (WATCH them blades, they can sting even when they're out of commission, like bumblebees) so the pawl slot is horizontal. Now take the pawl and put it in the slot so the flat side is *up* on the end that's in *front* of the axle (toward the front of the mower), and *down* on the end that's in *back* of the axle. The same rule follows for both pawls. (*Note:* Power reel mower owners—your pawls go the other way around, flat side down in front of the axle, up in back of the axle.)

Slide the pinion over the end of the reel axle and the pawl. Turn the pinion back and forth to make sure you have it right. The pinion should catch when you turn it forward (the same direction the wheel turns when you push the mower) and it should spin freely, with an oily clicking sound of the pawl, when you turn it backwards. (Power mower people—pinion should spin forward freely, catch in reverse.)

Put a little grease on the wheel axle, and on the bearing surface in the wheel. It doesn't take much, because those surfaces stay away from the water that dries up the pinion. Besides, the surfaces are sometimes made of oil-impregnated metal which lubricates itself. If the bearing surfaces are dry and scored, though (this will be the case only on very old or misused mowers), clean and then smooth the surfaces as much as possible with fine-grain emery paper. Grease them generously.

Hold the brush bar with one hand again and push the wheel onto its axle, turning it back and forth slightly so the gear teeth can engage (easy does it—you don't want to mow off your knuckles). Now turn the wheel as it would turn when the mower is going forward (power mower people—backward). Does the reel work? Try the other wheel for good measure—both wheels work the same way. If your newly reconstructed wheel is acting up, take it off again and recheck the pawl and pinion. Hold them in the positions like the blow-up view (illustration 4) to get things straight if you're working on a left wheel. To check a right wheel, hold the illustration up to a mirror, and the parts will all be switched around to where yours should be. Even the arrows showing the wheel direction will be correct. (Power mower people—you guessed it; the blow-up view is of your right wheel, as seen from the *front* of the mower. Use a mirror for the left wheel, and disregard the direction arrow.) It may be hard to read the writing in the mirror, but other than that you should be able to get the order of the parts straight.

If your wheel had a cotter pin or "C" ring, replace it and the washers under it.

For bolt-on wheels, stick the washer (if there was one) over the bolt and run the bolt through the wheel and axle. Add the nut washer, if there was one of those, and spin the nut on (cl), holding the bolt head in place with your finger. If the dog or shoulder was screwed up on your mower and you had to saw the bolt off, check to see if the hole in the end of the axle is OK. If the axle hole is as screwed up as the dog or shoulder on the bolt, take the remains of the bolt to a hardware store and get an equal size replacement bolt with a slotted head that you can use a big screwdriver on. If the axle hole is OK, just get a replacement bolt like the old one from a mower repair shop. Tighten (cl) the bolt securely.

Check the wheel's function again. Sometimes the final tightening will lock up a wheel whose parts aren't matched right. If there is no play in the wheel (you should be able to wiggle the rim about 1/8 inch, side to side) or if the wheel works very stiffly in forward or reverse, chances are the pinion you put in isn't the right size. Don't try to use the mower with the wrong size pinion in it. Get a better pinion. Then put the wheel together right and tap or screw the hubcap on if you have one.

Overhaul the other wheel if it needs it, and you can mow off into the sunset with a mower that glides easily when you push it, and makes that well-greased click-click-click sound when you back it up. (Power mower people— I know, I know, you click-click forward and glide backwards into the sunset. Go back to the *Power Reel Mower* section on page 59, to finish up.)

TIRE SHOT

Your kid locked the wheels on your mower and dragged the thing half way around the block to make a neato skid mark. Or you always run your mower along a sidewalk and it peels out at the corner like a drag racer. Or maybe you've left poor old mower out in the weather for so long

that the tires simply split in half. Whatever the cause, you
need to

CHANGE THE TIRE
To work on the tire, you have to get the wheel off the
mower. See the beginning of the *Wheel Overhaul* for how
to get the wheel off. You may notice right away, if you
unscrew a hubcap to get your wheel off, that your mower
is one of those nice simple ones with the hubcap holding
the tire to the wheel. You lucky dog. Take the cap and
tire off, get a new tire just like the old one, replace the
tire and hubcap on the wheel, screw in (cl) the screws,
and you're set to go.

    Of the more common tires which require complete
wheel removal, there are three basic types. One kind fits
in a rim that is shaped like a valley; another kind of tire
has a slot in it that fits over a ridge on the rim. The third
variation on the theme fits like a shower cap over a wide
flat wheel surface (see illustration 6a, b, c). The replacement of all three types involves following the same procedure. After removing the wheel, boil a kettle of water,
then put the hot water and the wheel in an old bucket

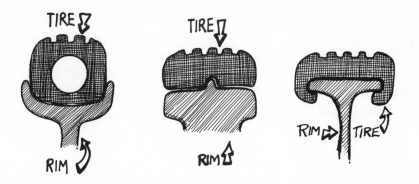

Illustration **6a, b, c**
Three common kinds of tire that require complete removal to change

(don't use the kitchen pan, the rubber taste will last for weeks). Let the wheel and tire sit in the hot water for about two minutes, so the tire can get warmed up. Take the wheel out of the water with gloves on, and peel the tire off. It's amazing how soft and pliant the rubber becomes. The heat, you'll notice, also expands the tire, making it even easier to pull off. Take the old tire, when it has cooled to its normal size, and go with it in hand to a mower shop for a replacement tire that's just the same.

To put the new tire on, give it the same hot water treatment. You don't have to heat up the wheel, just the tire. Let the assembled tire and wheel dry off and cool, then check to make sure the tire is good and tight. Put some extra grease on the pinion gear, the one that fits into the wheel's gear teeth; the hot water treatment tends to degrease the wheel, and that extra grease will replace what was lost. Replace the wheel as in the last part of the *Wheel Overhaul* procedure, and your mower will roll like new. It's best to replace both tires, even if only one is shot. That way the mower won't cut on a bias.

Reel and Cutter Bar

Description

The reel is the thing that spins rapidly when you push the mower. It is made up of a number of curved blades, which are held to the reel axle by three, four, or sometimes even five round metal spider plates. The reel axle turns on ball bearings which are either pressed into the side-plates of the frame of the mower, or held there by sleeves or brackets. The ball bearings are often covered by shields to prevent water damage (see illustrations 2, 13, 14).

The cutter bar, or knife bed, as it is often called, is a solid metal platform that runs from one side-plate of the mower to the other under the reel blades. It is held in place on each side-plate by a pivot bolt and one or two adjusting bolts (see illustrations 7, 8a, b, c, d, e). The cutter bar should be close enough to the reel blades that

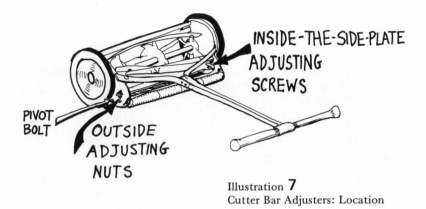

INSIDE-THE-SIDE-PLATE
ADJUSTING
SCREWS

PIVOT
BOLT

OUTSIDE
ADJUSTING
NUTS

Illustration **7**
Cutter Bar Adjusters: Location

a blade of grass cannot pass between the two at any point along the bar without being sliced. On some mowers the cutting action is achieved by having the blades actually graze the cutter bar in a scissoring motion. But on no mower should the blades whack against the bar.

Problems

REEL NOT CUTTING GRASS,
OR REEL HITTING BAR
Either the reel spins freely, but doesn't cut the grass, or the reel whacks against the cutter bar and makes it hard for you to push the mower. In either case, you should do a *Cutter Bar Adjustment* first, but remember that you might have to do the *Sharpening* procedure afterwards.

CUTTER BAR ADJUSTMENT
Before you can adjust your cutter bar you have to find out what kind of adjusting setup it has. If you're working on a power reel mower, disconnect the spark plug wire and ground it (see Frontispiece). Then, no matter which kind of mower you have, put it in a well-lighted place, standing in its normal mowing position. Turn the mower in such a direction that the light source is in front of the mower. Now get down on your hands and knees behind the mower (this may strike you as an abnormally humble

position, but it is the best one for acquainting yourself with the works of a lawnmower). Find the cutter bar, down almost under and just behind the reel. Notice that the ends of the cutter bar are attached to the side-plates of the mower by a number of bolts, usually two or three. One of these bolts on each end of the cutter bar is usually the cutter bar pivot bolt. If it is there, it will always be the bolt that is nearest to the ground, just behind the wheel. It goes through the side-plate and into the bar. Exception: on a few mowers, in place of the pivot bolt there is a short pivot axle sticking off the bar into a socket-like hole in the side-plate (see illustration 7).

There will be one or two other bolts holding the cutter bar in place. These are the cutter bar adjusting bolts.

If you have a spiffy modern mower, the adjusting bolt as well as the pivot bolt will probably come through the side-plate to the rear of the wheel, so you can adjust the cutter bar from outside the mower, without having to work with your fingers in close to the sharp reel blades (see illustration 7).

Your adjusting bolts are inside of the side-plates? Skip the next five paragraphs and go on to where inside-the-side-plate adjusting is covered.

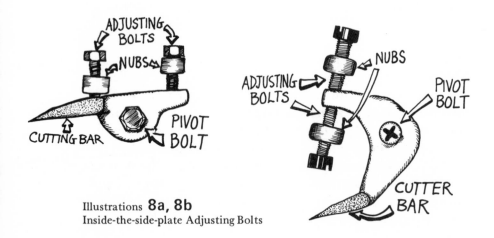

Illustrations **8a, 8b**
Inside-the-side-plate Adjusting Bolts

The outside-the-side-plate adjusting bolts come in three arrangements. On the two most common types, there is a bolt that goes through the side-plate to the trailing edge of the cutter bar, and a vertical threaded,shaft that goes up from this trailing edge bolt (see illustration 8c,d). On one of these two setups the vertical shaft is held in place against a nub on the side-plate by two nuts which lock against the nub from the top and the bottom. On the other common setup, the threaded vertical shaft disappears up into a single long hexagonal nut. The third, oddball outside-the-side-plate adjuster has a huge hexagonal bolt head that rests flush against the side-plate. A small trailing edge bolt goes through the big one and into the cutter bar. The small bolt is set off-center in the big one, so that the big bolt acts as a cam and moves the cutter bar up and down when turned (see illustration 8e).

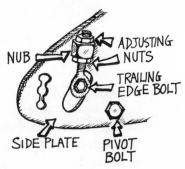

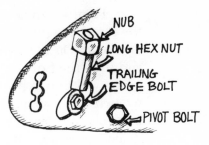

On all types of outside-the-side-plate adjusters, the adjusting procedure begins with making sure the cutter bar is free to move. Now the only way to be sure it is free is to loosen the pivot bolt and trailing edge bolt on each end of the cutter bar. These bolts are often held away from

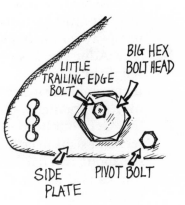

Illustrations
8c, **8d** and **8e**
Outside-the-side-plate
Adjusting Bolts

the side-plates by bushings (washers with sleeves that go through the bolt hole) so they won't bind up, but on most old mowers the bushings and bolts are rusted to the side-plates, holding the cutter bar stiff. So loosen (c-cl) all four bolts about a quarter turn. If you have trouble loosening the right side-plate pivot bolt counterclockwise, try loosening it clockwise, or backwards. God knows why, but some mowers use pivot bolts with reversed threads on the right side. Remember that you'll have to tighten that bolt counterclockwise if it has reversed threads. When the bar is loose, use the appropriate part of the paragraph below for twiddling with your adjusting bolt setup.

To move the cutter bar closer to the reel blades on the long hexagonal nut type, turn the long nut (c-cl) with a wrench. On the two nut type, you turn first the top and then the bottom nut (c-cl) with a wrench. On the big hexagonal bolt type, use a big wrench, like the Ford wrench or the channel lock pliers, and turn the big hex bolt (cl) to move the bar closer to the blades; hold it in its new position while you tighten (cl) the small bolt a bit to keep the big bolt still there. To move a bar that was whacking the blades away from them, the nuts on the vertical shaft adjusters must all be turned clockwise; the big bolt must be turned counterclockwise to move the bar away on the big bolt type.

Adjust both sides of the cutter bar equally. How to tell if the sides are equal? Easy. Turn the reel blades (watch them pinkies) slowly until the end of a blade is *exactly* over the leading or cutting edge of one end of the cutter bar. Get your head down near the ground just behind the reel and sight over the cutter bar. You should be able to see about two hair's breadth of space between the end of the bar and the blade. See the space OK? Good. Turn the reel just a bit so a blade has its opposite end exactly over the opposite end of the cutter bar. Check that end for the two hair's breadth. For those of you who have trouble visualizing two hair's breadth, and don't want to try pulling out two hairs and sticking them under there (or for

those of you who are bald), there's a slow but sure-fire
way to adjust the cutter bar perfectly.

Take two strips of newspaper, each about two inches
wide and a foot or so long, and slide them between the reel
blades and the cutter bar near each end of the reel (see
illustration 9). Adjust each end of the cutter bar until the
reel blades pinch or slice the newspaper, *without* whacking
the cutter bar. Take your time and twiddle the adjusting
bolts back and forth just a bit at a time. Move the blades
slowly with your fingers as you do the checking, and keep
your hands up near the brush bar so they don't get pinched
or sliced like the newspaper (see illustration 10).

You may notice that some of your reel blades come
closer than others to the cutter bar. That means the reel
is either bent or unevenly worn down. A good *Sharpening*
might help matters, but you may have to compromise on
your adjusting so that one or two of the reel blades just
brush the cutter bar at some point. *Don't* tighten things
up so much that any blades are whacking that bar, however.

When the bar is at its best position, tighten (cl) the
pivot and trailing edge bolts so it'll stay there. (Remember
that weirdo reverse-threaded pivot bolt on the right side-
plate? If you have one, tighten it counterclockwise.) On

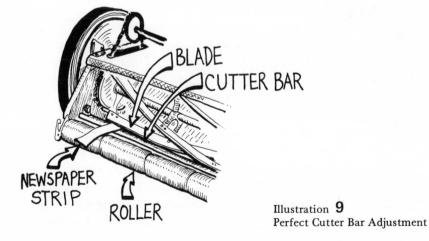

Illustration **9**
Perfect Cutter Bar Adjustment

27

the two-nut type adjusting setup, tighten both nuts against the nub; the top one tightens clockwise, the bottom one tightens counterclockwise. When everything is tight, do the newspaper test again to make sure the bar is still where you want it. Then push the mower (power mower people— pull the mower). It should glide along with the reel whirling around nicely, or it might make a slight scissoring noise if some of your blades were a bit out of line. If it makes loud clacking noises, or is hard to push, check the bar adjustment again. If the bar is OK, and the thing is still hard to push, maybe you have wheel problems. Go to the wheel section and find out. (Power mower people—you may have a tight clutch; go to clutch problems to find out.) Still hard to push the mower? Hmm. Maybe the mower is fine but you are feeling weak. Eat well, get a good night's sleep, and come back to the mower when you feel stronger. If the mower and you can both push and pull easily, but the mower still won't cut the lawn very well, go on to the *Sharpening* section in this chapter.

If you have *inside-the-side-plate* adjusting bolts on your mower, you have to be careful to keep your fingers clear of the blades during the whole cutter bar adjustment procedure. (Power mower people—double-check to make sure you unhooked and grounded the spark plug wire and disengaged the clutch.)

Find the pivot bolts. If your mower has them, they will be the only bolts which stick through the side-plates from the cutter bar (see illustration 7 for the general location of the pivot bolt). Loosen (c-cl) each bolt about a quarter turn so the cutter bar will be free to move. The pivot bolt will often have a bushing (a short sleeve of metal or plastic) that is supposed to keep it from binding on the side-plate, but the pivot bolt is usually so battered and rusty that you have to loosen (c-cl) it with a wrench to move the cutter bar easily.

There will be two bolts inside each side-plate for adjusting the position of the cutter bar (see illustration

8a, b). The heads of the bolts may be slotted for a screwdriver. Can you see both bolt heads from behind the lawnmower and above it? If not, it may be that one of the
bolts has its head facing forward. On a number of models,
the two bolts imprison an arm of metal that sticks up off
the cutter bar. To get at the head of the second bolt on
this type of setup, you either go around to the front of
the mower and look back through it, or tilt the mower
back on its roller (see illustration 2, or power mower
people illustration 22) and look between the roller and
the reel blades for the head of the second adjusting bolt.
Got both bolts in view now? Good.

The next question is which way each bolt moves the
cutter bar. Pick one end of the bar to work on for the
answer to this question. Look closely at the tips of the
adjusting bolts. Both should be touching the arm of the
bar. If they aren't, tighten (cl) them until they are. Use
a big screwdriver if there are slots for one, or a crescent
wrench if there are no slots. Bolts rusty? See *Rules of
Thumb*. Now take a close look (with your head down near
the ground so you can sight just over the back edge of the
cutter bar and along its upper surface) at the space between one end of the bar and the reel blades. Turn the
reel by hand, using the hand position shown in illustration
10 and keeping your fingers away from the cutter bar.
As the end of a reel blade passes the end of the cutter bar,
how much space is there between the two? It should be
about two hair's breadth. If the reel blade hits the end of
the cutter bar, or misses it by ¼ inch or so, you need to
adjust the bar for sure. But memorize that space there,
whatever it is. Then loosen (c-cl) one of the adjusting bolts
—it doesn't matter which one—by exactly one full turn.
Tighten (cl) the other bolt until it gets hard to tighten it
anymore. *Stop* tightening it at that point. You may be
moving the cutter bar right into the reel blades. See if you
can move the reel by hand again. If you can't, then you
can bet the bolt you were tightening is the one that brings
the cutter bar closer to the reel blades.

If tightening the bolt moved the cutter bar farther away from the reel blades, the bolt is obviously the "moving away" adjusting bolt, and the one you loosened must be the "bringing closer" bolt.

Get a felt pen, right now, before you forget which bolt is which, and make a big black dot on the head of the "bringing closer" bolt. Then you'll always be able to remember, or come back and look it up here in the book, to know for sure that the bolt with the dot on its head is the one which moves the cutter bar closer to the blades when tightened. Try the system out, right now, by returning the bolts to their original positions—remember, you loosened one by a full turn. Things back where they started? Good. Make a dot on the head of the "bringing closer" bolt at the other end of the cutter bar, so you can't get mixed up on that side of the mower either.

You're finally ready to start adjusting the damn thing. Loosen (c-cl) both bringing closer bolts one full turn. Tighten (cl) both moving away bolts completely. There should now be a sizeable space between the bar and the blades, no matter how things were when you started. Take two strips of newspaper, each about 2 inches wide and a foot long, and slide them into the nice space you have just made. Place one near each end of the bar, as in illustration 9. Make sure the reel is in such a position that the blades will come down against both strips of paper as the bar is moved up close. One blade will pinch one strip, a second blade must curve across the other end of the cutter bar where the second strip of paper is.

Loosen (c-cl) the moving away bolts (both of them) by two full turns. Tighten (cl) the bringing closer bolts by about a half turn at a time, alternating back and forth between the two, until some resistance is felt as you try to turn one of them. *Stop* tightening that bolt. Turn the reel very slightly. Is it pinching the paper strip? If it is, screw in (cl) the other bringing closer bolt until the bar pinches the paper on that side too.

30

If the bar doesn't pinch the paper when the bringing closer bolt runs into resistance, either the bar is hitting the tip of the moving away bolt, or the bar is adjusted all the way to the end of the range between the screws, and hitting the nub of the mower frame that the moving away bolt is attached to. Look closely for the tip of the moving away bolt in there. Is your cutting bar hitting it? If so, just loosen (c-cl) the moving away bolt another turn, and keep tightening the bringing closer bolt until the cutter bar pinches the paper. If your bar has moved all the way to the end of its range, but still is not close to pinching the paper, your mower is worn out. It has been sharpened so many times that the blades are too narrow to reach the bar. It's time to get a new mower.

Let's assume your mower is still usable; the cutter bar is pinching the newspaper at both ends. That means it is adjusted just right. To keep the bar in place there, tighten (cl) the moving away bolts until their tips just touch the cutter bar. Then tighten (cl) all four adjusting bolts against the cutter bar, turning each bolt just a tiny fraction of a turn at a time. That way, the bar won't move as you do the tightening. When all four adjusting bolts are tight, check to see that the paper is still being pinched by the blades and the cutter bar. If it isn't, adjust the bar by turning the bolts (moving away bolt c-cl, bringing closer bolt cl) slight amounts, like an eighth of a turn or less, until the paper strips are feeling the pinch at both ends of the bar. Finally, when the thing is adjusted just right, tighten the pivot bolt to freeze the bar in place for good.

Push the mower. It should either slice the strips of paper, or spit them out toward the back of the mower. As the mower rolls along, the reel should spin easily, making a delightful whirring noise. It's OK if some or all of the blades brush the bar very lightly, making a scissoring noise, but there should be *no clacking* noise. The clacking sound is the telltale sound of reel blades whacking against the cutter bar. Does your mower have the blade clackies? If so, make minute turns of all four adjusting bolts (moving away bolt cl, bringing closer bolt c-cl) until there is no more clacking.

Try the mower out. If it still won't cut the grass, go on to the *Sharpening* section below. If it cuts OK, but is hard to push and squeaky, try doing a quick lubrication job (see *Spring Checkup*, page 238). That doesn't help? Your wheels might be sick (see *Wheel Problems*) or the reel bearings might be shot (see *Reel Wobbly*, page 36).

ADJUSTED REEL AND CUTTER BAR STILL WON'T CUT GRASS

Your mower does everything perfectly except cutting the grass. Its blades spin easily and close to the ground (What's that? The blades are a mile above the grass? See *Cutting Height Adjustment.*) but it just don't cut the damn lawn. It's time for

SHARPENING

Or *lapping,* as the pros say. First of all, if you haven't adjusted the cutter bar as per the procedure directly above, do it. Even if the adjustment won't help the mower cut any better, it will at least line up the cutter bar so that it is parallel to the reel, which is a *must* before you can start sharpening. Cutter bar all lined up like it should be? OK. Is the mower still leaving most of the lawn uncut? Not OK. But easily cured.

Refresh your memory as to which cutter bar adjustment bolt is which, or if you have an outside-the-side-plate adjusting setup, recall which way it moves the cutter bar.

Loosen up (c-cl) the pivot and trailing edge bolts on the ends of your cutter bar if you have either, just as you had to do for the cutter bar adjustment (see illustration 7). Turn the reel by hand (watch the pinkies) until one end of a reel blade is close to one end of the cutter bar. Move that end of the cutter bar closer to the blades, by about a quarter to a half turn of whatever adjuster you have. This should bring that end of the bar and the blade into contact. Go to the other end of the cutter bar, and turn the reel by hand again (it'll be harder now, so be super careful of your fingers) until a blade at that end is right over the cutter bar. Move this second end of the cutter bar in until it is hitting the blade just like the first end.

Get some water-based valve-grinding compound from your local auto parts store. The more concentrated the stuff is, the better. Find a little paint brush to apply it with, or use your finger if you can remember to apply the compound *only* on the parts of the cutter bar where the blades aren't crossing it. Tip the mower back on its roller (see illustration 2 for hand mowers, illustration 22 for power mowers) and spread a thin layer of the grinding compound along the *front upper* edge of the cutter bar. This edge will probably be worn shiny. It is the edge that the blades are hitting, so WATCH YOUR FINGERS as you spread the goop. Don't turn the reel when your fingers are anywhere near the bar. When the whole shiny edge of the cutter bar has been gooped with compound (it'll only take about a half thimbleful for the job), go get a pair of gloves and put them on. (Power mower people—forget the gloves; all you have to do is turn the wheels backwards and the reel will turn backwards too.) Put the hand mower all the way back on its roller, and set your hands over the brush bar as in illustration 10. Being right-handed, I've always found that it's easiest to work from the right side

Illustration **10**
Turning the Reel

of the mower, holding the thing still with my left hand on the left side of the brush bar. You may want to pull the blades with your left hand, or with both hands. But the idea is to pull the blades up from the front of the reel so the reel turns backwards, grinding the blades and the cutter bar edge sharp. You should be able to hear the sharpening process taking place. It's a gratifying sort of sound, especially if you have the cutter bar adjusted evenly and it makes a nice constant gritty noise as you pull the blades up.

What's that? Your blades grind unevenly, sometimes slow and sometimes fast? Watch closely as you pull the blades up. Is one end of the cutter bar grinding the blades harder than the other? The cutter bar may need adjustment so it hits evenly all the way across. If the blades are grinding unevenly even though the bar is set properly, there are probably some warped blades, or maybe the bar is bent out of line. All you can do to straighten things out is keep grinding. If your blades and cutter bar are in good shape, the sharpening may only take ten to fifteen minutes of good hard reel pulling. But if you have a bent reel or bar, or a super-dull mower, it may take a long time. Boy those fingers get tired, don't they? If the bar is really bowed up or down, it may be a hopeless task. Some people think you can shim the cutter bar to straighten it; I don't. Take the mower to a shop for a professional grinding and alignment if it's badly bent.

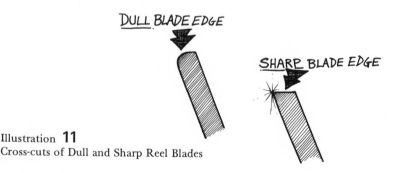

DULL BLADE EDGE

SHARP BLADE EDGE

Illustration **11**
Cross-cuts of Dull and Sharp Reel Blades

If you have passably good, straight blades and bar, keep turning the reel backwards until the gritty sound diminishes completely. Then put the mower under a bright light and look at the edges of the blades. If they are sharp, there will be a nice shiny surface that goes across the blade from one side of its business edge to the other. If the blade is still dull, you will be able to see a second plane or a rounded corner on the leading part of the cutting edge of the blade (see illustration 11). In bright light the rounded corner will reflect a dull line of light in addition to the shiny edge you sharpened. Look at several blade edges. Some will be sharper (have less of the rounded corner) than others. If they all look dull to you, go to a lawnmower shop and look at the blades of a new mower. That's what sharp looks like. Just one shiny surface along the edge of each blade, and no dull rounded corner.

If your blades are still dull after you have ground all the compound off, put a little more on the cutter bar, tighten the bar against the blades again, and keep pulling the blades backwards until you can't hear the gritty noise again. Check for sharpness. It may take two or even three repetitions of the sharpening process to get the blade ground down to a good sharp edge. If your fingers get too tired, leave the job and come back to finish it the next day, but do keep coming back to it until there's no dull corner left on each blade.

For a final test to make sure you have ground your blades sharp enough, rub your thumb very lightly *across* the edge, *not along* it. As your thumb moves across the edge, it should feel like it's rubbing over a ridge of microscopic jagged mountains. The edge shouldn't be bumpy, but it shouldn't feel smooth and rounded, either; it should feel as if there are minute points sticking up. Careful, now. If the bugger is sharp, each one of those tiny jagged points is going to want to cut you.

After you have sharpened the reel blades, take a wet rag and wipe all of the grinding compound off that's left on the blades and the cutter bar—if any stays on there, it

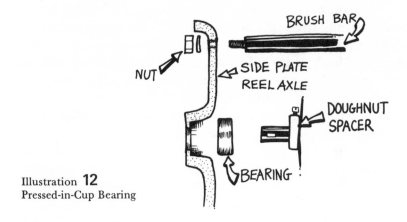

Illustration **12**
Pressed-in-Cup Bearing

will hasten the dulling of the blades as they spin forward when the mower is being used. The reel may need readjustment, so the blades are not only sharp, but two hair's breadth away from the cutter bar. Do the adjustment, and the mower will work like a dream.

REEL WOBBLY
You can't get your cutter bar close to the reel blades because the reel flobs around, either hitting the bar of missing it by a mile. To make sure that the problem is the reel, stop the mower, hold it still with one hand on the brush bar, grasp the reel blades firmly with the other hand, and see if you can move the reel on its bearings. Look closely at the places where the reel axle disappears into the bearings. If the axle is sliding in and out of the bearing more than 1/16 inch, or if the reel can move up and down on the bearings at all, then the bearings are probably shot.

Not all bearings can be replaced. To find out if yours can be, check around the axle where it disappears into the bearings. If there is a round plate with a flange holding the bearings in place, and if this plate is riveted to the side-plate with three or four rivets, you're in a jam. You can't get at the bearings (if it's hard to see the rivets in there,

36

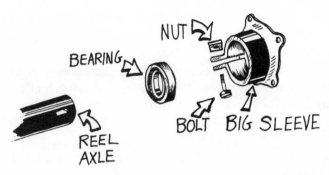

NUT

BEARING

BOLT BIG SLEEVE

REEL AXLE

Illustration **13**
Slots for Bearing Removal

look around the ends of the brush bar; if it's held by a riveted plate, the bearings will be, too). You have to take the mower to a shop with special rivet tools, or just give up and buy a whole new mower.

But if your loose bearings are held in a molded cup-like outcropping of the side-plate, and positioned on the reel axle by donut-shaped spacers with bolts through them, you can adjust or replace the bearings (see illustrations 12, 14). The bearings are also replaceable on models which have them held in place by a big sleeve with a binding bolt that sticks in toward the reel blades from the side-plates (see illustration 13).

On either kind of bearing setup, check whether the bolted positioners (the big sleeves or the donut-shaped spacers) are firmly held in place. The bolts on either type should be tight, so the reel can't slide back and forth. If the spacer bolts are loose, move the donut spacers as far away from the center of the reel as possible. On the big-sleeve setup, a shoulder or widening of the reel axle should push firmly against the bearing, holding it against the side-plate. Hold things in position as you tighten (cl) the bolts on either setup. Hard to do all those things at once in that small space, isn't it? Try holding the spacer until the bolt is just tight (cl) enough to keep it in place. Then let go of the spacer and get your hand out of the way so you can use a wrench or big screwdriver to get the bolt good and tight (cl).

If adjusting and tightening the positioners didn't remove the problem of wobbliness and your feel still flobs around on its bearings, it's time for

BEARING REPLACEMENT
In order to change the bearings, you have to take the whole mower apart to get at them.

Start with one wheel. Remove the wheel, pinion, and pawl assembly from one side-plate of your mower, following the first part of the *Wheel Overhaul* procedure. Keep all the parts together. Next loosen (c-cl) and remove the roller bracket bolt from the same side-plate (see illustration 12). Put the bolt back through the bracket and any washers and thread the nut on (cl) a few turns to keep those parts together and apart from the others. Loosen (c-cl for all but a few oddball mowers which loosen cl) the cutter bar pivot bolt and remove it. Loosen (c-cl) the trailing edge bolt(s) if the side-plate has any (see illustration 8c, d, e).

Take a look at the point on the side-plate where the handle is attached. Does the end of the handle simply fit onto a knob, pole, or lump of metal sticking out from the side-plate? Or is the handle end held on a stud by a cotter pin or nut? Remove the cotter pin by straightening the ends out and squeezing them together. Loosen (c-cl) and remove the nut if there is one, and put the small parts in a dixie cup where you won't lose them. Don't try to get the handle off its pole or stud yet. It will practically fall off when the side-plate is removed.

Check to make sure that all bolts holding the side-plate in place are loosened and removed *except* the brush bar bolt or nut (a little bolt through a sleeve, or a great big nut on the wheel side of the side-plate) which holds the brush bar to the side-plate. This is the last thing you undo (c-cl) to take the side-plate off. The actual removal may take some tapping and tugging of the side-plate, but don't hit the end of the reel axle—you might misshape it.

If you have the big bolted sleeve arrangement holding the bearings (see illustration 13), and the side-plate holds on stubbornly to the reel by the bearing after all the other bolts and nuts are removed, loosen (c-cl) the bolts in both big sleeves. Then you can remove the other wheel, pull both side-plates off the reel, and take the whole reel and bearing assembly to a mower shop for bearing replacement.

On all mowers that the side-plate came off easily, clean the removed side-plate off with gas and a wire brush. Look closely around the edges of the hole that the bearing is in, looking from the inside of the plate. If the bearing is pressed tightly into a molded cup in the side-plate, look for slots that go through the side-plate to the bearing (see illustration 14). To get the old bearing out of the plate, put the end of a bolt or punch or big screwdriver into one of these slots and tap it so it pushes the outer casing of the bearing. As the bearing begins to slip out of its cup, tap on the other side of it, setting the screwdriver or what-ever into the other slot, to keep things even so the bearing won't get jammed at an angle in its hole. If the bearing is in so tight that gentle tapping won't budge it, try putting

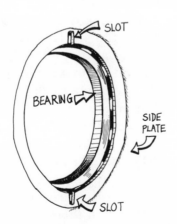

Illustration **14**
Slots for
Bearing Removal

the whole plate in a warm place, like over a heater or hot plate set on "warm," until it warms up a bit. Then take an ice cube or two in a plastic sack, and push them firmly against the bearing for a few seconds. The idea is to heat up the plate so the cup-shaped hole expands in diameter just a bit, then cool the bearings so they contract. When you have done this, try the tapping routine again. If the bearing is simply in that cup to stay for good, you can take it to a machine shop, where they will pop it out with a huge press for a nominal fee.

When you have the bearing out by hook or by crook, get its partner bearing on the other side of the mower out by repeating the *Wheel Removal* procedure, the gas and wire brush cleanup, and the tapping out routine. Don't undo the roller bracket, the cutter bar, or the brush bar on this side. You don't need to.

Take both bearings down and replace them with exact duplicate new bearings. Never replace just one. You'll have to go back and do the other one soon anyway. If you can get oil-impregnated replacement bearings, do so; you won't have to oil them.

To get the nice smooth shiny new bearings back in the side-plates, place each plate on a flat surface with the inside surface up. Clean the cups out with a solvent-soaked rag. Set the bearing so that it is sitting evenly on the edge of the cup. Get a wooden block and put it on top of the bearing. Tap the block gently, moving it back and forth so that the bearing goes in straight. If the bearing starts to go cockeyed, tap it back out as in the removal procedure. You don't want to bend and ruin your nice new bearing after all the trouble you have gone to already, do you? Use the side-plate heating trick if the fit is too tight. When the bearing is all the way into the side-plate, you will hear the tapping begin to resound with a louder pinging noise as the whole plate reverberates. At this point, give the block a couple of good whacks to get the bearing seated in flush where it should be. If the bearing slips into the cup all too easily, and is loose in there, you have the wrong size bearing. Back to the shop and get one that will fit tightly.

Begin *reassembly* of the mower by putting the reel axle and the pawl, pinion, and wheel back on the side-plate that still has the brush bar, the cutter bar, and the roller bracket attached (see the second half of the *Wheel Overhaul,* page 18, to get things together straight). Clean and lubricate any wheel parts that need it. Now put the wheel down flat on a table or the floor so the free ends of the cutter bar, the reel, the brush bar, and the roller are sticking up in the air. Get a willing friend (a very handy item to have around when you have to do jobs that require three or more hands) to hold the reel and the roller in place while you fit the side-plate over all those bars and axles and things. Thread the brush bar bolt (or nut) on (cl) a bit by hand, then start any bolts on the cutter bar if your mower has them. Finally, put the roller bracket parts back in place over the end of the roller or roller shaft, then put the roller bracket bolt through from the inside to the outside, and thread the nut on (cl). If you forget where the bracket for the grass catcher, the roller bracket, and any washers go on the bolt, look at the still untouched setup on the other side-plate. Now tighten (cl) all the bolts and/or nuts you have replaced so far. Check the reel to make sure it is seated on its bearings firmly. If the bearings are held in place by donut or big sleeve positioners, tighten (cl) the bolts so the reel will stay put.

Reassemble the last pawl, pinion, and wheel, following the second half of the *Wheel Overhaul* procedure. Clean and lubricate the wheel parts while you're at it, if there is any need.

When you're all finished, your reel should whirl merrily around when you push the mower, but stay quite still if you try to move it up and down or back and forth on the bearings. The cutter bar will probably be out of position, so to make a mower that not only whirs around merrily but also cuts the grass, go to the *Cutter Bar Adjustment* (page 23) procedure and get things in line.

Roller

Description

The thing that looks like a misplaced rolling pin. The
roller is a wooden, rubber, or plastic cylinder (or series of
in-line cylinders) that runs on a shaft across the back of
the mower and keeps it level so the blades will cut evenly.
The ends of the roller shaft are held by bolted, adjustable
brackets to the side-plates of the mower (see illustration 15).

Problems

ROLLER SHOT

Your old wooden roller has rotted away or has been eaten
by termites. Tip the mower over frontwards so the roller
comes up off the ground. Loosen (c-cl) one roller bracket
bolt and remove it slowly, watching the order of parts
around the bolt as they come off. Take the roller and its
shaft to a shop to get a replacement that's the same size.
If you can get a rubberized, high-impact plastic roller that
fits, do so. It needs little or no oil, and it'll last a damn
sight longer than the old wood one. Put one end of the
roller shaft back in the bracket that's still on the mower.
Arrange the parts of the other bracket around the bolt
and against the side-plate, in the same position as the
bracket you didn't move. Put the free end of the roller
shaft in its hole in the loose bracket, then tighten up (cl)
the bracket bolt and nut. You're set to mow.

MOWER CUTTING TOO HIGH
OR TOO LOW

Your mower either rides along so high over the lawn that
it leaves it about three inches tall so you have to mow
again in a couple of days (heaven forbid!) or it cuts so
close to the ground that it pulls the grass out by the roots
and makes a bald spot out of every little lump in the
lawn's surface. If your mower has the latter, cutting-too-
close problem, you may notice that it often bogs down,

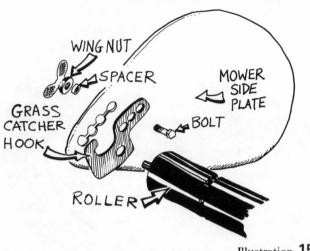

Illustration **15**
Roller Bracket Parts

causing the roller to lift up off the ground. Whether the thing is riding too high or cutting too close, you need to do some

CUTTING HEIGHT ADJUSTMENT

Before randomly twiddling bolts and levers on your mower to try to adjust its cutting height, find out just what adjusting mechanisms it has. First check the roller brackets. These usually have two or three holes in them, or a slot that allows you to move the roller bracket bolt to any of a range of positions (see illustration 15). Sometimes there are not only several positions in the roller bracket, but also several holes or notches for the bracket bolt where it goes through the side-plate of the mower (see illustration 15). For mowers with these simple roller adjustments only, see *Roller Adjustment,* below.

More elaborate mowers have several holes in the side-plate for the wheel axle. Look inside the side-plate for these holes (see illustration 16). The whole wheel can be removed and shifted up or down, thus raising or lowering the cutter bar and reel in relation to the ground. Finally, at the top of the line, there are the mowers that have two levers or even a single knob that can raise or lower the wheels (see illustrations 17, 18). For these snazzy mowers,

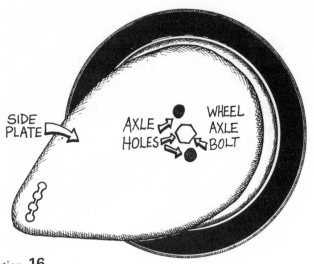

Illustration **16**
Wheel Axle Height Adjustment

go to the paragraphs on *Wheel and Roller Adjustment*.

No matter which kind of height-adjusting gismo your mower has, take it to a flat concrete surface, like a patio or a garage, to do the adjusting.

ROLLER ADJUSTMENT

On simple mowers with wheels that can't be moved up and down, the extent to which you can change the cutting height is limited to about a one-inch range, because the way you do your height adjustment is by tipping the mower forward or back with different roller positions. Any mower works best at a near-level position. Unless your blades are worn down almost to their limit (see *Cutter Bar Adjustment*), the mower will be close to level with the roller bracket bolts near the middle of their range. Are yours near the middle? If the bolts are near the bottom of the brackets (a lot of each bracket is sticking up above the bolt) and/or near the top of the range in the mower side-plate, then the roller will be up too high. The reel will be so close to the ground that it will catch or mow bald spots. Also, the reel will be tipped back by the high roller position, making the cutting action inefficient.

If the bolts are too near the top of the brackets, and/or too near the bottom of the side-plate range, the roller will be too low. The back of the mower will be way up in the air so the reel can't cut the grass.

Tip the mower forward so the handle is on the ground and the roller is up in the air (power mower owners —see illustration 23). Loosen (c-cl) the roller bracket bolts and position the brackets so the bolts go through the middle of the range, whether that means in the middle of a curved slot, or in the middle of a number of notches or holes. What's that? You have two or four notches? You have to make a tough decision. Which end of the range should you put the bolt closer to? First try the hole that's on the far side of the middle of the range from where the bolt was to start with. If this over-corrects the problem you were having, try the other hole that's closest to the middle.

The same principle works for fixing the bolts in their holes or notches in the side-plate of the mower. Keep the bolts near the middle of the range, first trying the position at or just beyond the middle one from where the bolt was to start with.

Tighten (cl) the roller bracket bolts when you have them positioned equally. If the same bolt that holds the roller bracket also holds a little L-shaped hook for the grass catcher, keep this hook in place, too, while you tighten (cl) the bolt. The job may seem to require six or seven hands—try holding the bracket and hook in place and tightening (cl) the bolt just with your bare fingers first. Then let go of the bracket and hook and concentrate on tightening (cl) the bolt with a wrench. Turn the mower back right side up (power mower people—get the mower off its blocks) to make sure you positioned the roller brackets equally. If both wheels of the mower are sitting on a flat surface, both ends of the roller should be resting on it, too. Roller a little cockeyed? Look closely at the positions of the bracket bolts in both the bracket and side-plate ranges. Find the differences of position, loosen (c-cl) one of the bolts, preferably the one that's farthest from the middle of its range, and reposition things so that they are exactly the same as the other side. Tighten up (cl), and check again on the flat surface.

Take your newly adjusted mower out for a try. On some very old mowers, the roller may still be too low (the mower will miss most of the grass). For this exceptional case, you have to reset the roller bracket bolts so the roller is near the top end of the range and most of the bracket is sticking up above the bolt.

WHEEL AND ROLLER
ADJUSTMENT
If you have a mower with not only roller but also wheel adjustments for cutting height, or if you were sent here from the *Cutting Height Adjustment* paragraph above, you can adjust your mower's cutting height to a very fine degree. But remember that for every change you make in the wheel position you *must* change the roller position in the same way to keep the mower parallel to the ground.

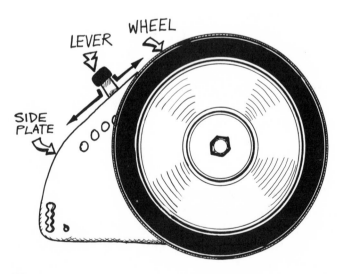

Illustration **17**
Lever Height Adjustment

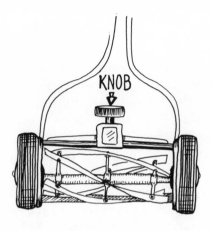

Illustration **18**
Knob Height Adjustment

A mower that isn't running horizontally won't cut well, and some power reel mowers won't run at all if they are tipped forward or back too much.

There are three kinds of adjustable wheels found on common mowers. The most primitive kind has a number of holes in each side-plate for the wheel axle bolt. Look on the inside of the side-plates; you should see the nut on the end of the wheel axle. If there are other holes in a line with the one that the axle bolt is sticking through, then you have the *move-the-axle* type adjustment (see illustration 16).

If you can see no row of axle bolt holes on the inside of the side-plate, but rather long curved slots, chances are that you have a *lever-adjustable* wheel. Look for the levers sticking up or up and back out of the top of spaces between the side-plates and a smaller plate on which the wheel is mounted (see illustration 17).

What? You have neither an axle bolt showing inside the plate nor levers sticking up? You either have a super-simple mower with no axle bolt at all, or you have a super-fancy mower with a *single knob* adjustment which will be prominently sticking up above the reel on two special brush bars (see illustration 18).

No matter which kind of adjustment setup you have, get oriented before you start shifting the wheels up and

down. Take the mower to a hard flat surface like a patio, garage, or sidewalk. Get down on your hands and knees, and look under the reel from the front of the mower. See the cutter bar back under there? Just look at it, don't stick your finger in there and point at it. You might lose a pointer or two. Observe, from a safe distance, how high the cutter bar is off the ground. Get an accurate measurement; take a ruler or yardstick and put it straight up and down between the reel blades, so it winds up just in front of the cutter bar. Look again under the reel from in front of the mower, and you can read the ruler and see how many inches the cutter bar is off the ground. This is the cutting height. Write it down here
so you won't forget. Remember as
you do the rest of the procedure that to move the cutting height *up*, you are going to move the wheels *down* in relation to the rest of the mower. To *lower* the cutting height, you move the wheels *up*. Backwards from what you might think at first. If the number you wrote down was more or less than 1–2 inches, you are probably going to want to move the cutting height into that range.

On *move-the-axle* type mowers (see illustration 16) it's easiest to change the position of the wheels with no weight on them. Tip the mower back on its rollers (see illustration 2; power mower people, see illustration 22). Pry the hubcaps off the wheels, or unscrew (c-cl) the cap screws if your mower has hubcaps over the wheel axle bolt. Look at the bolt head in the middle of the wheel. It may have a hex shape or a cotter pin through it, or it may have big wings on it so you can turn it by hand.

The winghead type bolt is easy to use. Loosen the bolt (c-cl on most mowers, but cl on the *left* wheel of some mowers) about two full turns. Move the wheel back and forth in its range (on some fancy jobs there is a handle that makes this wheel moving easier) and figure out which way moves the wheel down in relation to the mower, and which way moves the wheel up. Adjust the position of the wheel as you need to, either *down* to raise the cutting height, or *up* to lower the cutting height. Don't set the wheel at either extreme of its range unless you absolutely have to. The mower will always work best near the middle of its height range. When you have the wheel where you want it, tighten (cl, most likely, or c-cl on those odd left wheels) the axle bolt and move around to the other wheel to repeat the change. Make sure you put both wheels in the same position. To check, set the mower back on its wheels. If one doesn't hit the ground without tipping the roller cockeyed, then you haven't got the axles in the same position. If the wheels are even, go on to the *Roller Follow-up* section below, and your mower will soon be cutting smoothly at its new cutting height.

Does your mower have a movable axle with either a simple hex bolt head or a cotter pin through it? Now it's your turn to move that thing to a new cutting height. Loosen (c-cl) the bolt and the nut that's on the other end inside the side-plate, and take the nut and the washer that's probably under it off. Or take the cotter pin out. Put them where you won't lose them. Hold the wheel in place with one hand, and pull the bolt so that it slides out just enough to free the wheel from its position hole. Easy does it. Just wiggle that bolt out a bit at a time until you feel the wheel is free. Then move the wheel, *up* to lower the cutting height, *down* to raise the cutting height. Push the bolt out through its new position hole, replace the washer, and tighten (cl) the nut back on the bolt thoroughly. Move the wheel on the other side of the mower in the same way, making sure to set both axle bolts in the same height hole. To check the positioning, put the mower back down on its wheels. If only one wheel hits the ground, or if the roller goes all cockeyed when both wheels touch the ground, something's out of whack. Check the wheel axle bolts and get them in the same holes. Don't forget to do the *Roller Follow-up,* as on the next page, to level your mower at its new height so it will cut smoothly.

49

For *lever-adjustable* wheels (see illustration 17) the procedure is quite simple. Tip the mower back on its rollers (see illustration 2; power mower people, see illustration 22). Push one of the levers horizontally to disengage the positioning knob. When the wheel is free to move up and down, jockey it around to figure out which way moves it up in relation to the mower and which way moves it down. On a few models, you'll notice that the lever is not free to move the wheels—these models all have wingbolts in the middle of the wheel; loosen (c-cl) the wingbolts, then do the positioning as usual. Push the lever to position the wheel as needed, remembering that to raise the cutting height, you move the wheel *down* in relation to the mower, and to lower the cutting height you lift the wheel *up*. Set both wheels in the same position, then check to make sure you have it right by setting the mower back down on its wheels. If the roller is cockeyed, or if one of the wheels doesn't come down to the ground, reset it so it's even with the other. When the wheels are in equal positions, tighten (cl) the wing-bolts if you had them, and you're set to go on with the *Roller Follow-up* below, to level your mower at its new cutting height so it will cut smoothly.

Mowers with a *single knob* adjustment for cutting height make it very easy on you (see illustration 18). Just turn the knob and watch the cutter bar under the reel to see how high or low you are making it. The knob adjustment shifts not only the position of the wheels, but that of the roller as well, so you don't even have to do the *Roller Follow-up*. Pretty nifty, huh? The only trouble with the system is that it makes for a little extra weight, which you have to push around the lawn every time you mow it.

ROLLER FOLLOW-UP

After setting your cutting height to where you want it, put the mower down on its wheels on a flat, close-to-level surface again. Measure the cutting height with the vertical ruler like you did before. You did change the height the way you intended to, didn't you? If not, don't worry, just do it over. You won't be the first guy who has had to do something twice. There is a mechanic's theorem called "Murphey's Law" which states that any mechanical procedure which *can* be done backwards, *will* be done backwards

Measure the distance that the cutter bar has been moved when you have it where you want it. To keep the mower level, you have to move the roller the same distance, and just like before, if you moved the wheels *down* to raise the cutter bar, you have to move the roller *down* in relation to the rest of the mower. If the bar moved down, the roller has to go *up,* just like the wheels did. Got it? Your mower may have numbers or letters for the wheel positions and the roller bracket positions, and a little chart that shows what goes with what to keep the mower level at different cutting heights. Fine. But if the numbers wear off, or if you lose or forget the chart, just come back to this procedure to get things straight.

Follow the *Roller Adjustment* procedure to move the roller to where it should be. Test the mower out. If you have moved the roller the wrong way, it will either be so far up that the reel cuts bald places in the lawn, or so far down that the mower doesn't cut at all. Readjust the roller if you need to, so your mower will run on an even keel and cut the lawn to the length you want.

Handle

Description

The part of the mower you keep your hands on when you're cutting the lawn. It usually consists of a crossbar that is shaped or that has grips to fit your hands, a shaft, and a pair of metal braces that attach to studs (poles or nubs) on the side-plates of the mower. Sometimes all the different parts are replaced by a single steel tube or a pair of tubes that are bent into the proper shape (see illustration 19).

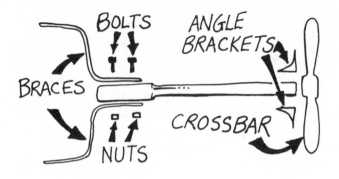

Illustration **19**   The Handle

Problems

HANDLE FALLS OFF

The whole handle assembly slips off the mower side-plates.
First check what kind of stud (pole, or nub) the end of
the handle braces fit onto. If there is supposed to be a
cotter pin through a little hole in the end of the stud, and
the pin is mangled beyond recognition or gone altogether,
then you need a new pin (a nail will do in a pinch if you
put it on and bend it into a Z shape). Put the brace in
place and stick the pin through its hole, then bend the
arms of the pin around the stud so the brace can't come
off.

   If your mower's braces aren't held in place with
cotter pins, they have to be held on there by pressure.
The braces must be stiff and pushing against the side-
plate firmly.

   Try wiggling the braces back and forth in relation to
the shaft. Is there some play between the three parts?
There shouldn't be any at all. Tighten (cl) the two brace
bolts that go through the handle shaft until the whole
assembly is stiff. On one-piece tubular handles, the stiff-
ening may be done by taking the end of the brace off its
stud and stretching it either out (if the stud is on the
inside of the side-plate) or in (if the stud is on the outside
of the side-plate). Be careful not to stretch the tube so

much that you crimp it. Replace the end on the stud with equal care. If the thing is hard to get back over the stud, that's a good sign. It'll stay there once you get it on.

To prevent the braces coming loose again, try to use the mower without twisting violently on the handle, or pulling sideways with it.

HANDLE ROTTEN OR BROKEN
An old mower with wooden handle parts can have some loss due to age. The sad thing is, it's usually impossible to find replacement parts for your beloved old mower. If the shape of the broken or rotten part is relatively simple (i.e., a square or round cross-section shaft, or a dowel-shaped handle end), then you can have the part made by a good mill shop. Have them make the part out of oak or hickory. It'll cost, but when you're attached to your good old mower, it's worth the price of a transplant, right?

If the part has a complicated shape and will call for all sorts of fancy millwork, or if you don't really care a fig for the old mower, you might as well get another mower, or look around for another old handle that will fit the studs on yours.

Grass Catcher

Description
The floppy canvas basket with a metal bottom that drags along behind the mower and catches the clippings. It is held to the side-plates by two L-shaped hook brackets.

Problem
CATCHER FALLING OUT OF HOOKS
The catcher is rubbing on the roller and getting pushed up and off the hooks that stick off the side-plates. If these hooks are adjustable, all you have to do is loosen (c-cl) the bolts that hold them and slide them back in their slots so

the hook arm trails farther behind the roller. Tighten (cl) the bolts, holding the hooks in place so the hook arms point up and slightly forward. To make sure the hooks are in the same position as each other, put your head down near the ground, sight across the back of the mower along the roller, and line up the two hook arm tips.

If your mower doesn't have adjustable hooks, you can try to find a catcher that will fit them better. Some catchers have wire loops that stick forward from the front of the metal bottom, so that the catcher trails an inch or so behind the roller.

Illustration **20**
Power Mower—Fertilizer Unit

Chapter 3
Power Reel Mower

A power reel mower is nothing more than a normal hand mower with a motor on top of it that drives the reel blades. Whereas on the hand mower the slowly turning wheels make the reel spin at a high rate, on the power reel mower the rapidly spinning engine turns a sprocket which is attached to a large sprocket on the reel—this makes the reel spin about one-third to one-half as fast as the engine, which is still very fast. The rapid spinning of the reel is reduced to a slow wheel speed by the wheel pinion gears, so the mower doesn't drag you around the lawn at 30 mph.

Shopping Hints

The basic attributes of a good power reel mower are a simple, powerful, four-stroke engine, big wheels, oil-impregnated bearings, and simple height and roller adjustments. See the *Engine* chapter for specific hints as to just which engines are best. Nine-inch wheels are adequate, but ones with diameters of 10 or 10½ inches are best. Read the description of the mower or ask the salesman whether the bearings are oil impregnated. It's pretty hard to tell from the outside of the mower, but if the bearings are oil impregnated, it'll save you some messy lubrication.

If you're looking at mowers with adjustable cutting height attachments, make sure it's easy to move both the wheels and the roller to different positions in relation to the body of the mower. If there is a hand lever sticking up from the top plate of the mower just inside each wheel (see illustration 21), this lever should be the one that controls the position of the wheel. Tip the mower back on its roller, just enough so the wheels leave the ground, and have somebody hold the thing that way. Try changing

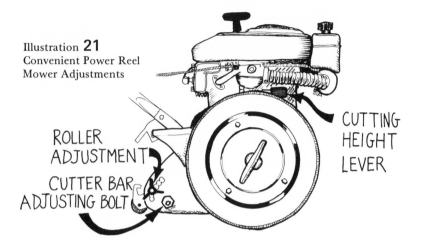

Illustration **21**
Convenient Power Reel
Mower Adjustments

CUTTING
HEIGHT
LEVER

ROLLER
ADJUSTMENT

CUTTER BAR
ADJUSTING BOLT

the wheel position. Is it easy to do? Put the wheel back in the position you found it. Was that easy to do? Sometimes the lever has to be shoved and wiggled one way or the other, or its mounting bolt might need loosening to release the wheel from its position, but the changing process should be simple once you have the hang of it. Put the mower back down on its wheels. Both hitting the ground like before? If not, get the wheels positioned right before some crabby store manager kicks you out of the place.

Check the ease of roller adjustment by tipping the mower forward just enough that the roller comes off the ground. If there are wing nuts holding the roller in place, great (see illustration 21). Loosen (c-cl) one and move the roller around, then set it back where it was and tighten (cl) the nut. Did the system adjust easily? It should. If either the wheel or roller position adjustments are hard to get at or tricky to work (on some models you have to take the whole wheel apart to change its position, for instance) then either plan on leaving the cutting height at its standard position, or look for a more convenient mower.

While you're looking at adjustments, check to see where the cutter bar ones are. They should be on the *outside* of the side-plates, away from the blades and out where you can get at them (see illustration 8c, d, e). If they are on the inside of the side-plates, as on most old hand mowers, you'll have one hell of a time adjusting that cutter bar right.

Check the handle for sturdiness by trying to twist it. The power reel mower needs the strongest handle of all mowers, because the machine is the heaviest and most willful. You don't want it to come loose and let the mower go dancing off through the tulips.

For a general idea as to whether a new mower is safe or not, look for a triangular decal on the handle or the deck that holds the engine. This decal, or seal, which says American National Standards Institute on it, won't guarantee you a safe mower, but it means that at least some basic safety measures have been taken.

The grass cutting part of the power reel mower is almost exactly like that of the hand mower. With that in mind, most of the procedures below will simply refer you to those for the hand mower. But before you start treating your power reel mower like a push-mower, TAKE ITS POWER AWAY! That means disengaging the clutch completely, so that the reel and the engine can spin independently, and disarming the engine as well. Disconnect and ground the spark plug wire (see Frontispiece) before you start working on the wheels, the reel blades, or the roller. That way, the thing can't start up and mow you without warning.

Wheels

Description

The round things that always seem to be peeling out and digging ruts in the lawn. Working from the outside toward the center of the mower, each wheel consists of a hubcap (often missing), the metal body of the wheel and the tire, the toothed inner rim of the metal wheel body, a bearing surface which turns on the axle, and a cotter pin, "C" ring, or bolt which holds the wheel on the axle.

A small pinion gear turns the wheel, getting power from the engine via the reel and a "pawl," a flat pin that runs through the reel axle inside of the pinion (see illustration 4). The pawl in the pinion of a power reel mower is in the *opposite* position from the pawl in a push mower, because the energy comes from the reel to the wheel, not from the wheel to the reel. (Remember, it's reel to wheel, not wheel to reel, cha-cha-cha.)

The entire wheel assembly is either attached directly to the side-plate of the mower, or to a separate plate, which can be moved up and down in relation to the mower, to adjust the cutting height.

Problems

WHEELS WON'T TURN

First make sure the problem is with the wheels. Leave the engine off and push the mower forward. Does it roll? If not, then something is indeed wrong with the wheels. With the engine still off and the clutch disengaged, roll the mower backwards. If one or both of the wheels turn backwards without turning the reel, then you know the wheels are in trouble. But if the wheels lock and can't turn the reel, you probably have reel and cutter bar problems and should go on to that section. If the whole system, wheels and reel, works fine in reverse with the clutch disengaged, but then won't work going forward with the engine on, then the problem is with the clutch or chain. See the *Clutch and Chain Description* below.

If you are sure your problem is in fact a wheel problem, tip the mower back on its rollers until the wheels just leave the ground. Put blocks under the front of the mower to keep it in that position. On many models an eight-inch cinder block (see *Tools* in Appendix) under the front edge of the deck of the mower will do the job beautifully (see illustration 22). On other models it's easier to back the mower up near a wall and pull the handle down to where you can tie it to a nail or something to keep the wheels up off the ground. Check the clutch for disengagement, and ground the spark plug wire (see Frontispiece).

Now you can treat your power reel mower just like a hand mower, and do the *Wheel Overhaul* procedure on page 15 under *Hand Mower*. When you have completed the procedure, try the wheels out with the clutch still disengaged. Roll freely with that nice clicking sound when you push it forward? Good. Do the wheels spin the reel blades merrily when you pull the mower backwards? Great. If not, first try spinning each wheel back and forth to check the pawl positions. Remember, the power reel mower should have its pawls in the reverse position from the hand mower. If the wheels want to work, but are held up by a sticky reel, then see *Reel Problems.* If the wheels and reel all seem OK now, hook the spark plug back up and start the engine to see if the whole system is together right. If it isn't, first check the wheels you just worked on, then check the reel, and finally the clutch for problems. Go to the sections for each of those parts, in that order.

Illustration **22**
Wheels Tipped Up

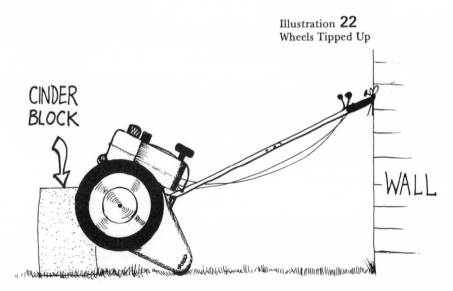

CINDER BLOCK

WALL

TIRE SHOT

Your mower has been peeling out so long that it has not only dug ruts in your lawn, but also worn its tires down to the bare metal. Tip the mower back on its rollers and either block or tie it there, as in illustration 22. Undo and ground the spark plug wire, then turn to the *Change the Tire* procedure for hand mowers, page 21.

Reel and Cutter Bar

Description

The reel is the thing that spins like crazy when you engage the clutch. It consists of a number of curved blades, which are held to the reel by three, four, or sometimes even five round metal spider plates. The reel axle turns on ball bearings which are pressed onto the reel axle and either pressed or riveted into place in the side-plates of the mower frame. It's usually hard to see these bearings because they are often covered with metal shields to protect them from water damage. On higher-quality mowers the bearings are made of oil-impregnated bronze or steel so that they never need lubrication (see illustrations 13, 14).

The cutter bar, or knife bed as it is sometimes called, is a solid metal platform that runs from one side-plate of the mower to the other under the reel blades. It is held in place on each side-plate by a pivot bolt and one or two adjusting bolts, which can move it closer to or farther from the blades. The bar must not be hit by the blades, but it should be close enough to them that no grass passes between the two without being cut (see illustrations 7, 8a, b, c, d, e).

Problems

REEL NOT CUTTING GRASS,
OR REEL HITTING BAR

Either the reel spins freely, but doesn't cut the grass, or the reel whacks and clatters against the cutter bar. DON'T USE A MOWER WITH A CLATTERING REEL! The engine will drive the blades against the cutter bar so hard that both will soon be bent and "rippled" completely beyond use. If your bar is rippled, you will be able to see the undulations if you look closely at the shiny surface on the leading edge of the cutter bar. The undulations can be taken out only by professional machining, so you have to take the mower to a shop and face the music. It'll be plenty expensive enough to keep you from letting it happen again.

To stop a cutter bar from clattering, or to adjust a cutter bar that won't cut the grass, you have to do the *Cutter Bar Adjustment* (page 23) in the *Hand Mower* chapter first, but remember that you may have to do the *Sharpening* routine afterwards (page 32).

If, after you have adjusted the cutter bar, you are sent back here for testing because you can't tell if your reel is working right, reconnect your spark plug wire, start your mower up, and see if it cuts the lawn OK without making horrible clacking noises. If the clacking persists, STOP the mower immediately and go back to try more cutter bar adjustment. If the bar adjustment has no effect, go to *Reel Wobbly,* below. If the thing adjusts fine, but still doesn't get the lawn cut, go right on to

ADJUSTED REEL
WON'T CUT GRASS
The mower works beautifully, except that it leaves half the grass uncut. If the cutting height isn't too high (see *Mower Cutting Too High or Too Low* under *Roller,* below) and the cutter bar is adjusted, then it's time for

SHARPENING
(Or *lapping,* as the pros say.) Before you start the sharpening procedure, make sure the cutter bar is aligned just right. That way you will start sharpening things evenly. Then prop up the mower as in illustration 22. Go through *Sharpening* in the hand mower section (page 32), remembering that when it comes to turning the reel backwards,

you have it *much* easier than the hand mower people. You can simply turn the wheels backwards and that will make the reel go the way you want it to. No fuss, no muss, no missing fingers. Your arms may get tired if you have to do a lengthy sharpening, but that's no long-term problem.

REEL WOBBLY

The mower clatters and makes strange whining noises, and if you have adjusted the cutter bar, you have found the adjustment to be of no use, because the reel blades whack the bar and wander away from it mindlessly. As a result, a completely random pattern of gouged holes appears when you try to mow the lawn. Disengage the clutch on the mower and pull the spark plug wire (see Frontispiece) to make sure the mower can't start up while you're fiddling around down among the reel blades. Hold the brush bar or the leading edge of the deck of the mower with one hand, and grasp the reel with the other. Careful. Those blades can be sharp. See if you can move the reel laterally on its bearings. Lateral movement is not good, but the mower will still work with a little of it, and on some types of mower the lateral play can be adjusted away. Next check for any up and down play. If you can feel any movement of the reel on its bearings in the vertical plane at all, you're in bad trouble. You'll have to replace the bearings, and this means taking the entire mower apart.

Before you despair, though, try a couple of simple solutions. Tip the mower forward as in illustration 23. See if you can wiggle the side-plates of the mower. The bolts that hold the side-plates to the deck, the brush bar, the cutter bar, and the roller might all be loose. There may be loose rivets holding these parts together, which you can't do a thing about; in that case, the mower is shot. But if your mower has loose bolts, all you have to do is tighten (cl) them thoroughly. The bolts that hold the side-plate to the deck and the brush bar are sometimes

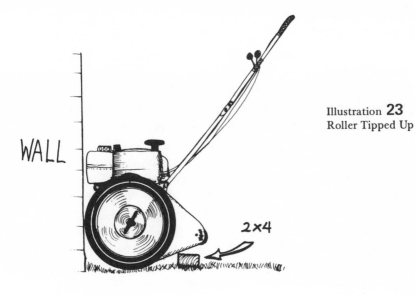

WALL

Illustration **23**
Roller Tipped Up

2×4

behind the wheels. To get at these bolts, you have to block the front of the mower up off the ground (see illustration 22), and remove the wheels, one at a time, as per the *Wheel Overhaul* procedure (see page 15) in the *Hand Mower* chapter. Tighten (cl) the bolts when you have the wheel off, then reassemble the wheel as in the last part of the *Wheel Overhaul* procedure. Some of the bolts may be very hard to get at between the reel and the inside of the side-plate. Try getting to them with an open end wrench from behind the reel, then from in front of the reel or even from below the reel, sliding the wrench up in a vertical position along the side-plate until it gets to the bolt. All you have to do is hold that bolt or nut still in there as you tighten (cl) from the more convenient other side of the side-plate.

Bolts all tight? Good. Reel still loose? Baaad. One last-ditch effort can be made, if you have a particular type of mower with handy bearing holders. Look at the end of the reel axle that doesn't have the sprocket on it, just inside the side-plate of the mower. Do you see a big sleeve with a binding bolt through it like in illustration 13? If you do, you're in luck. Skip the next paragraph and see what you can do to tighten up the buggers.

If you don't have the big-sleeve bearing holders, you probably see just a bearing set into an inset cup in the side-plate, like in illustration 14. Or you might see a metal shield around the bearings that's riveted to the side-plate. The riveted setup (those rivets may be hard to see; look around the ends of the brush bar—if it's riveted to the side-plate, the reel bearing holders will be, too) is impenetrable. There's no way you can adjust or replace those loose bearings. You can try a good lawnmower shop for professional help, but you'll probably have to get a new mower. If your mower has loose pressed-in bearings like those in illustration 14, you cannot adjust them, but you can do the *Bearing Replacement* procedure below if you're up to it.

For those of you who are lucky and have the big-sleeve type bearing holder as in illustration 13, first take a big screwdriver and check to see if the bolts that bind the sleeve onto the bearings are tight. The slotted head of each bolt is toward the rear of the mower. Stick the big screwdriver between the reel and the side-plate and get it in place on a binding bolt. Tighten (cl) the bolt thoroughly. Check for reel wobble. Did that tightening get rid of it? Don't worry if there is a little side-to-side wobble left. That won't affect the cutter bar adjustment. Just pray that there isn't any up-and-down play left in the bearings. If there is, go on to that monumental task described below, the

BEARING REPLACEMENT

Each reel bearing probably costs about a dollar or two. But to get at the reel bearings to replace them, you have to do something like fifteen to twenty-five dollars worth of labor, figuring on paying yourself two bucks an hour. So before you decide to tackle the job, take a look at the general condition of the machine. Is the engine a real smog belcher? Are the blades bent and the cutter bar rippled (see *Reel Hitting Bar,* under *Reel and Cutter Bar*)? If the mower has a number of serious problems, you should simply replace it. It won't be worth the big bearing replacement job. But if the rest of the mower is in good shape, and you have lots of time and patience to spend taking the thing apart, and no money to spend on a new mower, let's get at it!

There are two basic ways that power reel mower frames can be attached together. One way is to have the top deck wrap around the side-plates. The other way is to have the deck bent at right angles inside the side-plates. As you will see in illustrations 24a and b, the bent-inside-the-side-plate deck makes it easy to undo the side-plate and remove it horizontally so you can get at the reel bearings. On that nasty wrap-around-the-side-plate arrangement, though, you have to lift the engine and deck up off the mower before you can remove the side-plate. Take a close look at the joint of the deck and the side-plate on your mower. Look for a triangular outcropping at the back of the deck; this is the part of the deck that will bend down to wrap-around-the-side-plate. Figured out which type of frame joint your mower has? Fine. Go to the appropriate *Side-Plate Removal* section below.

SIDE-PLATE REMOVAL,
BENT-INSIDE-THE-SIDE-PLATE DECK

Take the mower to a flat place, like a garage floor or a patio (*not* a lawn, where you will lose lots of small parts). Block up the deck of the mower so both wheels and one end of the roller (the end nearest the chain and sprocket on the reel) are off the floor (see illustration 25). Remove the wheel on the completely raised side as in the first part of the *Wheel Overhaul* (page 15) in the *Hand Mower* chapter. Put the wheel, the pinion, the pawl, and any other small wheel hardware all together in a box or in the recessed shape of the wheel, and keep them somewhere safe so they don't get mixed up with the other parts you will be dismantling. Put a felt pen mark, L or R, on the pinion so you'll know whether it's the left or right one later on.

Loosen (c-cl) and remove the bolt that holds the roller bracket to the side-plate. Take the bracket off the side-plate and roller and put the bolt back through one of the bracket holes. Replace any washers, spacers, or grass catcher hooks around the bolt that were around it before, and thread the nut on (cl) a few turns so you don't lose any of that stuff.

If there are any bolts sticking through the side-plate attached to the cutter bar, loosen (c-cl) and remove them, putting them with any accompanying washers in a cup or something to keep them separate from everything else. If your mower has the big sleeves with binding bolts holding the reel bearings, as in illustration 13, loosen (c-cl) both bolts so the reel and bearing unit will be able to slide out of the sleeves.

Take a look at how the mower handle is attached to the inside of the side-plate. If it is held on its stud (pole) in there by a cotter pin or a bolt and nut, remove the pin or the nut; the pin type is often hard to get at, and if you mess up the pin while trying to get it squeezed together and out of its hole, make a note that you have to get a new pin as well as the bearings. Don't undo both sides of

Illustration **24a**
Deck Construction

WRAP-AROUND-THE-
SIDE-PLATE-DECK

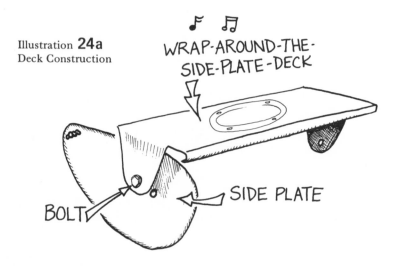

BOLT

SIDE PLATE

the handle. You only need to have the one side free to get at the bearings, and if you leave the handle in place you won't break the control wires that lead up to it.

Loosen (c-cl) and remove the bolts that go through the side-plate and into the deck and/or brush bar. These should be the only bolts left holding the side-plate to the rest of the mower. Make sure the mower deck is blocked up well, then gently twist, wiggle, and tap the side-plate free of the mower handle and any other bars or axles sticking through it. If the sprocket hangs up on a little upside-down U (a sprocket scraper), or a metal shield, unscrew (c-cl) the screws through the side-plate that hold either one in place, and take it off so you can get that side-plate off. Put the deck and brush bar bolts back into their holes and thread the nuts on (cl) a couple of turns so you don't lose them.

Remove the remaining wheel from its side-plate, and take the pawl out of the reel axle. Mark the pinion with a felt pen, L or R, so you'll know which one it is later. Finally, take the reel out of that bearing, lifting the chain off the sprocket as you go. If the bearings stay attached to the reel, but pop out of their cups in the side-plates, that's OK—just take the whole reel and bearing unit to the shop for bearing replacement.

Illustration **24b**
Deck Construction

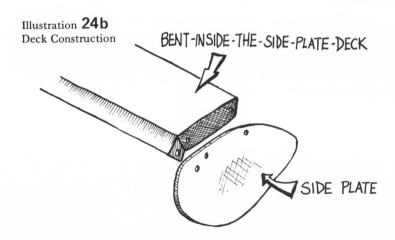

BENT-INSIDE-THE-SIDE-PLATE-DECK

SIDE PLATE

Illustration **25**
One Side Raised Up

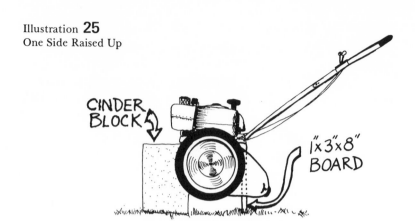

CINDER BLOCK

1"x3"x8" BOARD

SIDE-PLATE REMOVAL,
WRAP-AROUND-THE-SIDE-PLATE DECK

To remove the side-plate, you are going to first take the deck and engine off the top of the mower, then work on the reel and side-plate system independently.

Start by undoing the chain that goes from the clutch down to the reel. To get at the chain you may have to remove a shield that is over it. Undo (c-cl) the metal screws or bolts that hold the shield down, take the shield off, and start (cl) the screws or whatever back into their holes in the deck. To undo the chain once you have gotten access to it, find the master link and push the removable side off its rivets as in the *Chain Exchange* procedure (see illustration 31). Pull the master link out of the chain and get the whole messy chain off its sprockets. Put the master link back onto one end of the chain and pop the removable side back into place so you don't lose it. Keep the chain in some dust-free place like a shoe box so it won't get any gunkier than it already is.

Find out how your mower handle is held in place. It will probably be held by a cotter pin or a bolt and nut on a stud (a pole) mounted on the inside of the side-plate. If that's the case, back the mower up near a wall and tie the handle up so it'll stay in the position it rests in (see illustration 26). You want the handle to stay put so the

68

control wires don't get stretched or bent as you work on the mower. Undo the cotter pin (bend and squeeze the ends together or cut them off, then pull the thing out with pliers) or the bolt and nut (c-cl). Use the big screwdriver to pry the handle ends off the studs. Put the pins or bolts and nuts in a safe place where they won't get lost, like an old jar or dixie cup. If the cotter pins got mangled in the removal process, make a mental note to get new ones when you go to get your bearings.

Get a friend and a couple of 8x8x16 inch cinder blocks (see *Tools* in Appendix), or a reasonable facsimile (wood blocks and an orange crate that'll add up to an 8-inch platform will do), and prepare for the big lift-off. Position yourself *exactly* as in illustration 27. I know it looks awkward, and feels awkwarder. But after many tests and aching backs, it was found to be the best position for the job. Make sure your elbows are braced against your bent knees, and try lifting the weight of the deck and engine off the side-plates. Lift with your legs and arms, *not* your back. You won't be able to lift the top of the mower completely off, because of the last two bolts you left through the side-plates (you *did* leave them there, didn't you?), but just see if you can hoist the weight of the thing. If it's too much for your size, admit it, and

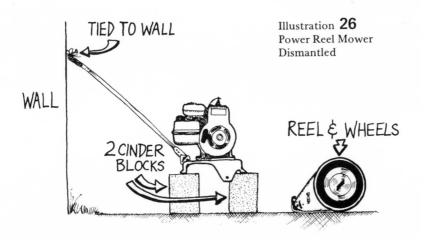

TIED TO WALL

WALL

2 CINDER BLOCKS

REEL & WHEELS

Illustration **26**
Power Reel Mower
Dismantled

ask your handy friend if he can do it. Especially if he's a *big* friend. You don't want to break your back just to replace a fifty-cent bearing, after all.

When you and your strong friend are all set for the Big Lift, take the nuts off (c-cl) those last two bolts and lift the deck and engine, pulling the last two bolts out of the wrap-around as you do so. If the bolts are hard to pull out past the tires, grab them with a pair of pliers or the vise grip and *pull.* When the two halves of the mower are free of each other, quickly roll the lower half out of the way and slide the cinder blocks under the deck and set the bugger down before you (or your ex-friend) pop a gut. Put those last two bolts back into the holes in the wrap-around deck and thread the nuts on (cl) so you can't lose them.

Now you can take the reel-wheel assembly apart to get at those shot bearings. Start by removing the wheel and pinion-pawl gismo which are on the same side as the chain sprocket. Follow the procedure in the first half of the *Wheel Overhaul* (page 15) in the *Hand Mower* chapter. Put the wheel and all of its parts together so you won't mix them up with other parts. Mark the pinion gear with a felt pen, L if it's the left one, R if it's the right one, so you won't mix it up later either.

Loosen (c-cl) and remove the bolt that holds the roller bracket to the side-plate. Take the bracket off the side-plate and the roller and put the bolt back through one of the bracket holes. Put any washers, spacers, or grass catcher hooks that were around the bolt back on it in order, and thread the nut on (cl) a few turns to keep all those parts in a group.

If there are any bolts sticking through the side-plate attached to the cutter bar, loosen (c-cl) and remove them. Keep them together with their washers, if any, in a dixie cup or something. If you have the big-sleeve bearing holders as in illustration 13, loosen both binding bolts so the reel and bearings can slide out.

Loosen (c-cl) and remove the bolts that go through

Illustration **27**
The Big Lift

the side-plate into the brush bar. These should be the only bolts left holding the side-plate to the rest of the mower. Pull, tap, and gently wiggle the side-plate off the end of the reel axle and the cutter bar. Is a little upside-down U plate or a shield over the sprocket hanging up on it? Unscrew (c-cl) the screws that hold either one to the side-plate and take the thing off. Put the brush bar bolts and washers back into place in the holes on the end of the brush bar, and thread the nuts on (cl) a turn or two so you don't lose them.

Finally, take *just* the wheel off the other side-plate, so you can take the pawl off that end of the reel and take the reel out altogether. Mark the pinion again, L or R, whichever it is.

If you feel like it, go have a beer and take a breather. You've earned it, for crying out loud. Then come back and do the

BEARING EXCHANGE
First see what's holding your shot bearings in place. Are the bearings simply pressed into a cup-like outcropping

in the side-plate, or are they held in a big sleeve with a bolt binding it tight? See illustrations 12, 13, 14. If the whole side-plate is covered with grass and gunk, clean it off with solvent and the wire brush, so you can see which bearing holders you have.

If your mower has the big sleeves with binding bolts, take the reel and bearings to a mower shop and have them pull the old bearings off the reel axle and press new ones into place. Don't forget cotter pins if you need them to replace those you ruined in the dismantling procedure. When your reel has nice new bearings set on it, go back to the *Reconstruction* section for whichever kind of side-plate setup you have.

If your bearings were pressed into cups in the side-plates, but came out of their cups and stuck to the reel axle, take the whole works to a shop and have them pull off the old bearings and press new ones into place. Get cotter pins if you need them, and go on to the *Reconstruction* procedure for your type of mower.

Exchanging pressed-in bearings that stay in their side-plate cups instead of coming off with the reel axle is trickier. First work on the side-plate you took off the rest of the mower. Find the slots for tapping the bearing out, like in illustration 14. Put a screwdriver or punch in one of the slots and tap the bearing. If it budges, tap in the other slot and work back and forth, tapping each side of the bearing out a bit at a time so you don't get the thing jammed in there at an angle. If the bearing doesn't budge at all when you tap it, try warming the side-plate over a heater or on a hot plate set at "warm," and cooling the bearing with ice in a plastic bag. This should spread the side-plate and shrink the bearing just enough to let you tap it out. If all else fails, you can take the whole side-plate to a machine shop, where they will press the goddam thing out with a huge press for a nominal fee. When the bearing in the accessible side-plate is out, tap out the bearing that's in the side-plate you didn't dismantle. Careful. Don't knock the mower off its blocks in the process.

Take the bearings to a good mower shop or a bearing shop and get exact replacements. To fit the nice shiny new bearings back in the cups, first clean the cups completely, then set a bearing so it is resting flat on the rim of a cup. Put a piece of wood against the bearing and tap the wood gently, moving it back and forth and watching the bearing to make sure it goes in straight. You don't want to bend it after all the work you have done to get to this point. When you have tapped the bearing all the way into place, it will make a louder pinging noise as the whole side-plate begins to resound with each blow. With both bearings tapped all the way home, you're ready to go on to the *Reconstruction* procedure for whatever type of side-plate setup you have.

RECONSTRUCTION,
BENT-INSIDE-THE-SIDE-PLATE DECK

Start by putting the end of the reel axle that doesn't have the sprocket on it into the side-plate that's still attached to the rest of the mower. Push the axle and the bearing in just far enough so that the pawl slot appears on the out- side of the side-plate. Slip the chain into place on the sprocket so the other end of the reel will stay put. Stick the pawl in place, with the slot horizontal so it won't fall out. The flat side of the pawl must be *down* in *front* of the reel axle, and *up* in *back* of the reel axle. Got it? Check to make sure. Put the correct (you did mark it, didn't you?) pinion on and spin it back and forth. It should turn freely forward (the way the wheel turns if the mower is going forward) and catch in reverse. If the pinion catches when spun both ways, first check the pawl again, then see if you switched the pinions of the two wheels. If you marked the pinions, you won't have them mixed up, but if you blew it, just switch the pinions now before you go any further. Complete the reassembly of the wheel, using the procedure in the second half of the *Wheel Overhaul* section in the *Hand Mower* chapter (page 18).

Slip and wiggle the side-plate you took off the mower

back over the end of the reel axle, and the end of the cutter bar, too. Place the handle end over its stud. Push the bolts that hold the side-plate to the deck and the brush bar back through their holes, and start (cl) the nuts on the threads. This may be a very awkward job. If the handle keeps pushing the side-plate out of place, pull the two ends of the handle toward each other and tie a rope tightly between them. If you can't get the bolts and/or nuts in between the reel and the side-plate with your hands or a pair of pliers, try putting a little roll of sticky tape on the end of the blade of the big screwdriver, and sticking the bolt or nut there as in illustration 28. You can push the bolt through its hole in that tight place with this setup, or (if the bolt comes through from the outside) hold the nut in there if you have to while you just get the bolt started threading onto it (cl). Once you have the bolts and nuts all started, tighten (cl) them completely with wrenches. If you tied the handle ends together, untie them now, and put them over their studs. Put the cotter pin or bolt and nut on the handle stud, so the handle can't come off.

If you have a mower with the bearings held in sleeves by binding bolts, center the reel; tap it back and forth until the bearings are sunk equally far into the sleeves, then tighten (cl) the binding bolts so the bearings are held firmly in place. Check for play. If there is any, take the side-plate off again, take the bearings out, and get ones that fit the reel axle and the sleeves tightly.

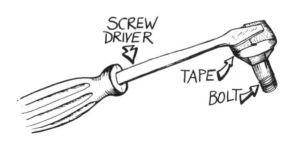

Illustration **28**
Bolt Holder

If you took any bolts out of the end of the cutter
bar, replace them (cl) now. Undo (c-cl) the bolt and nut
that are in the loose roller bracket. Put the bracket in
place on the end of the roller shaft. Put the bolt through
the same hole in the side-plate that the bolt on the other
side-plate is through, and position the bracket like the
other one, too, so your roller won't be cockeyed. If you
have forgotten the order of the washers and things on
the bolt, check the one on the other roller bracket. If
you unscrewed a sprocket shield or an upside down U
sprocket scraper, screw it (cl) back on now.

Replace the remaining wheel (remember—flat side
of the pawl *down* in *front* of the axle, *up* in *back* of the
axle), using the second half of the *Wheel Overhaul* procedure in the *Hand Mower* chapter. Check the mower to
make sure the reel works smoothly without play. The
cutter bar may be out of adjustment, so do the *Cutter
Bar Adjustment* procedure in this chapter. When you're
finally finished, go celebrate. You won't have to hassle
with those bearings for a looong time. Especially if you
keep them oiled.

RECONSTRUCTION,
WRAP-AROUND-THE-SIDE-PLATE DECK
Start by sticking the end of the reel axle that doesn't
have the sprocket on it into the side-plate that still has
the cutter bar and the brush bar attached to it. Push the
reel axle and the bearing in just far enough so that the
pawl slot appears through the side-plate. Get that slot
horizontal, then slide the pawl into place, with the flat
side *down* in *front* of the reel axle, and *up* in *back* of the
axle. Got it? Check to make sure. Put the correct (you
did mark it, didn't you?) pinion on the reel axle. Spin the
pinion back and forth. It should spin forward (the way
the wheel turns when you push the mower forward)
freely, and catch in reverse. If it catches when you spin
it both directions, first check the pawl to make sure you
got it in right, then try switching the pinions if you blew

it and forgot to mark them. Finish putting the wheel on as described in the second half of the *Wheel Overhaul* procedure in the *Hand Mower* chapter.

Take the bolts out of the free end of the brush bar, the ones you left there for safe keeping, and put the side-plate you took off in place over the end of the reel axle with the sprocket on it. Wiggle, slide and tap the plate over the end of the cutter bar and up to the end of the brush bar. Put the bolts and nuts through their holes in the side-plate and brush bar. This can be pretty awkward. If you can't get a bolt and/or nut in place with your hands or a pair of pliers, take a piece of sticky tape and make a little roll of it on the end of the big screwdriver blade to hold the bolt or nut as in illustration 28. You can poke the screwdriver into that narrow space between the side-plate and the reel, and either push the bolt into its hole, or hold the nut while you start (cl) the bolt from the out-side onto the threads. Tighten (cl) all of those bolts and nuts thoroughly with wrenches.

For those of you who have bearings held in big sleeves with binding bolts, center the reel; tap it back and forth until the bearings are sunk equally far into the big sleeves, then tighten (cl) the binding bolts, so the reel will stay put. Check for play in the bearings. If there is any up-and-down play, take the damn side-plate off and do the *Bearing Exchange* procedure again, making sure you buy the *exact* same size bearings as the old ones this time.

If you took any bolts out of the end of the cutter bar, replace them (cl) now. Undo (c-cl) the bolt and nut that are in the loose roller bracket. Put the bracket in place on the end of the roller shaft. Stick the bolt through the same hole in the side-plate that the bolt on the other side-plate is through, and position the bracket like the other one, too, so your roller won't be cockeyed. If you have forgotten the order of the washers and things on the bolt, check that on the other roller bracket as well.

If you took a sprocket shield or upside-down U

sprocket scraper off in dismantling the side-plate, screw it (cl) back in place now.

Replace the remaining pawl, pinion, and wheel (remember—flat side of the pawl *down* in *front* of the reel axle, *up* in *back* of the axle). Refer to the second half of the *Wheel Overhaul* (page 18) in the *Hand Mower* chapter. Test the wheel and reel outfit by pushing it backwards on the floor. The reel should spin merrily, and coast when you stop pushing.

Now you're about set for the big lift again (see illustration 27). Undo (c-cl) the two bolts and nuts that you put through the holes in the wrap-around portion of the deck. Give the two bolts to your friend so he can hold them at ready. Lift the engine and deck half of the mower just off its cinder blocks and have the friend slide the blocks out and roll the wheel and reel half of the mower back in place. Settle the deck down over the brush bar so that the holes and/or studs on the bar and side-plate match up. Hold it there while the friend quickly puts those two bolts he's holding (aack! where in the hell did he put them?) into their holes, and threads (cl) the nuts on a bit. You can stop grunting and hefting. Tighten (cl) all the deck bolts thoroughly, using the method in illustration 28 to replace any awkward, hard-to-reach bolts.

Put the ends of the handle back over their studs on the side-plates, and replace and tighten (cl) the bolts and nuts or bend the cotter pins to keep the handle in place.

Undo the master link of the chain and put the chain back on the sprockets, resetting the master link as in the *Chain Exchange* (page 94). Replace the shield, if there was one, and screw in (cl) the screws that were holding the shield to the mower.

The cutter bar is probably out of whack a bit, so see the *Cutter Bar Adjustment* (page 23) and get that taken care of.

Good gott! You did it! Try the mower out and if it works, celebrate. You have done the biggest job there is to do on your mower: Congrats!

Roller

Description

The thing that looks like a misplaced rolling pin, and trails along at the back of the mower. It consists of a cylinder or a number of cylinders, made of wood, rubberized plastic, or rubber. It turns on a shaft that is held by adjustable brackets, which are attached to the side-plates by bolts.

Problems

ROLLER SHOT

The problem and its solution are both exactly the same as those described in the *Roller* section of the *Hand Mower* chapter. Go there and take care of your ruined or rotted roller (pages 42–51).

MOWER CUTTING TOO HIGH
OR TOO LOW

Either the mower is riding along a couple inches above the top of the grass and "fanning" it down flat instead of mowing it, or the mower is grinding into the ground all the time, peeling out, cutting gaping bald spots in the turf, and generally tearing hell out of things. For either problem, the solution is a good

CUTTING HEIGHT ADJUSTMENT

Before you can adjust the cutting height, you have to find out what mechanisms your mower has for doing the adjusting. Look inside the side-plates where the wheel axle bolt comes through (see illustration 16). It will be hard to see that place if your mower has a big shield over the top and front, and a shield over the chain at one end of the reel, but put your head down near the ground so you can see back in there. Using the big screwdriver, scrape any dried grass and dirt off that's caked around the wheel axle bolt and nut. If there is just the one axle bolt hole, the one that the bolt is stuck through, and no row of other holes or a long slot around that bolt, then you have a mower with *Roller Adjustment.* Tip the mower forward a bit and block it up there as in illustration 23. Do the *Roller Adjustment,* (on page 44) as for the hand mower. But keep in mind that power mowers work best with the engine close to level. That means you should always keep the top deck of the mower level if the mower is sitting on level ground. You can check with a wood-worker's level before and after you do the roller adjust-ment. You are severely limited in how far you can adjust the cutting height, but for most normal lawns, the middle of the cutting height range is the best place to set the mower anyway.

If your mower has several axle holes for the wheel axle, or a slot that allows the axle to be raised and lowered in relation to the mower body, then you must do the *Wheel and Roller Adjustment* (page 46) for *Hand Mowers,* and do a measured, even adjustment of both the wheel position and the roller position. After you have done the adjusting, check with a level to make sure the deck is still parallel with level ground, so the engine will run smoothly.

Clutch and Chain

Description

The engaged clutch and chain deliver the power of the engine to the reel. If the clutch is disengaged by the remote control on the handle, the power train is interrupted, and the reel and wheels stop while the engine goes on running.

If your *mower either won't get its ass into gear, or can't get out of gear,* then you got troubles with the clutch and/or chain.

Maybe the engine starts and runs OK, but the mower either runs away from you the minute you get it started, or it stops when you go through any thick grass, even though the engine keeps grunting away in desperation.

The problem can be with any or all of the following four units: the control lever, the wire or rod, the clutch mechanism, or the chain.

Before you get into finding out which unit is sick, turn off the engine and disconnect the spark plug wire so you can't get yourself too wrapped up in the problem (see Frontispiece). If your clutch and chain have any shields over them that look simple to remove, undo (c-cl) the screws that hold the shields to the deck, and get them out of your way. Turn the shields upside down and put the screws and washers in them so nothing can get lost.

Look at the place where the clutch control wire or rod is joined to the clutch, and move the control lever back and forth. Is the clutch wire or rod moving the mechanism visibly? If it isn't, or if the wire or rod is obviously bent, broken, or completely loose so that the lever wiggles freely, see the *Clutch Control Lever and Linkage* section below. If the lever is inhibited so it can't move all the way to the extremes of its range, see *Wire or Rod Adjustment* (page 88).

Take a look at the chain. Is it broken or thrown off its sprockets? If it is, see the *Chain Problems* below. If the whole clutch mechanism is loose, sliding around on the mower deck randomly, so that the chain gets loose and then tight, see *Chain Adjustment* under *Clutch Mechanism Problems* (page 98).

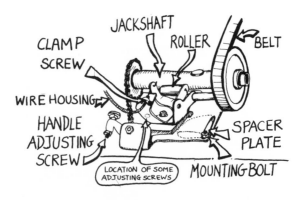

Illustration **29a**
Dead Man Clutch

80

Most clutches use a black rubber belt. If the belt stays loose or stays tight no matter what position the clutch is in, or if the belt is broken or deformed so that it doesn't turn on its pulleys smoothly, see *Clutch Mechanism Problems,* page 98. If the engine is cool (if it hasn't been running for a while), grab it firmly and see if it will move around on the deck. Engine hotter than snow in Orange County? Wait until it cools off, or use gloves to see if it's loose. Engine loose? Go to *Mechanism Adjustment* on page 102 and get it tightened up in the right place. If the clutch jams or is sluggish, go to the *Clutch Mechanism Problems* section, pages 106–108.

Clutch Control Lever and Linkage

Description

The clutch control consists of a lever or a knob that's attached to the mower control panel, which in turn is bolted to the mower handle. A housed Bowden wire (a wire in a length of coiled housing that looks like a long narrow spring) or an open rod runs from a hole in the end of the lever to the clutch mechanism. At the

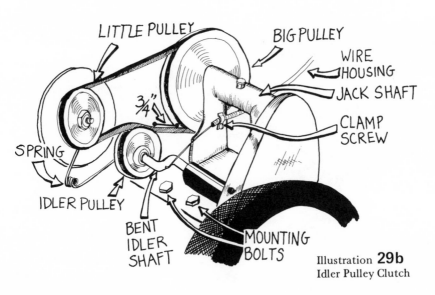

LITTLE PULLEY

BIG PULLEY

WIRE HOUSING

JACK SHAFT

3/4"

CLAMP SCREW

SPRING

IDLER PULLEY

BENT IDLER SHAFT

MOUNTING BOLTS

Illustration **29b**
Idler Pulley Clutch

mechanism, if the linkage is a wire, the wire housing is held by a clamp screw, and the end of the wire has a Z bend in it or an anchor bolt that holds it in a hole in the clutch mechanism (see illustrations 29b, d, and 30a). On mowers with the open rod linkage, the end of the rod at the control lever usually has a right-angle bend and is held in place with a cotter pin. The other end often has threads, and is fitted with a threaded sleeve and locknut for adjustment, but sometimes it is held by a bend and cotter pin like the lever end (see illustrations 29c, 30b). On a few models, the clutch is controlled by moving the handle itself up and down. On these mowers the handle pushes against an adjustable bolt, which in turn moves a pivoted arm (called a dead man) that is attached to the clutch mechanism (see illustration 29a).

Problems

WIRE OR ROD DISCONNECTED

One end of the wire or the rod has come out of its hole. The rod should have a cotter pin hole through one end. If it does, and the pin is gone, just get a new pin that fits

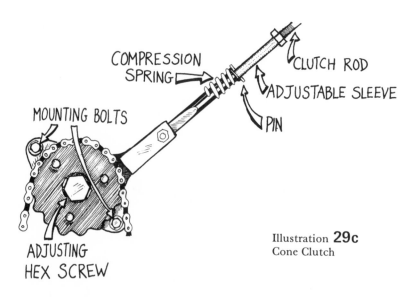

COMPRESSION SPRING

CLUTCH ROD

ADJUSTABLE SLEEVE

MOUNTING BOLTS

PIN

ADJUSTING HEX SCREW

Illustration **29c**
Cone Clutch

through the hole (1 inch by 3/32 inch is the most common size), put the rod back onto its big hole in the lever or the clutch mechanism, and push the cotter pin into place, bending its ends around the rod so it can't come out again. If the end of the rod is threaded, a sleeve must be turned back up it and locked into position against a locknut.
If this puts the clutch out of adjustment, see *Wire or Rod Adjustment* (page 88).

If, on a wire control, the wire has come out of its hole either in the lever or in the clutch mechanism, the repair can be trickier. Check the end of the wire. Is the Z bend still there? If the end has broken off, so there's just an L bend left, all you have to do is bend the L into a Z again as in illustration 30a.

To reset the Z in its hole, you may need a little free wire. On the mechanism end of the wire, simply loosen (c-cl) the clamp screw and pull the housing out from under it so you can curve the wire around and guide the bent end into the hole with a pair of needlenose pliers. At the

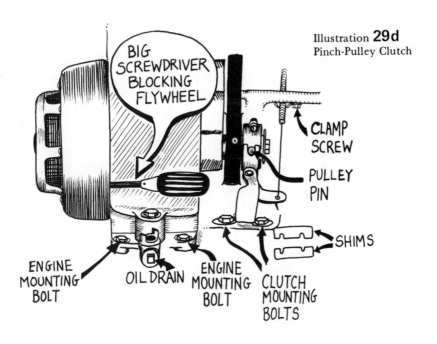

Illustration **29d**
Pinch-Pulley Clutch

lever end of the wire it's often easier to undo (c-cl) the bolt that holds the lever in place, and work the lever over the end of the wire. Retighten (cl) the lever bolt so that the lever is just barely free to move, and therefore stays put when you leave it in a given position. Put the lever all the way to the extreme that makes the wire stick out its longest at the mechanism end. Make sure the mechanism is at the right extreme, then set and tighten (cl) the clamp screw. Try the clutch out to make sure the wire can move the clutch from full on to full off. If it can't, see *Wire Adjustment* (page 88).

WIRE BROKEN

If just a bit of the end of the wire is broken off, see *Wire Disconnected,* above. But if a whole segment of the wire is broken off, it must be replaced. Loosen the clamp screw that holds the end of the housing at the clutch mechanism, and take the Z end out of the hole if any of it is left there. If part of the wire is left in an anchor bolt, loosen (c-cl) the bolt about one turn, and pull the piece of wire out. Pull all that remains of the wire out of the housing. Straighten the housing and measure it. If it is all bent and unraveled, take it to be replaced. You will have to get a wire that is at least 6 inches longer than that housing. If the wire has a knob on the end of it, take the knob with you, and go with the remains of your old wire to a mower shop, preferably one that deals in the kind of mower you have. If you can get a precut wire and housing kit, do so, but don't be surprised or discouraged if you have to buy just a length of bare wire, then cut and bend it yourself.

Attach the control lever end first. This involves threading one end of the wire all the way through the housing from the control lever end. It may be hard to push the wire through. Grease it, and straighten out any minor kinks or sharp corner bends in the housing. Push the wire all the way through the housing, though, so at least 3 inches are sticking out both ends. Back the wire

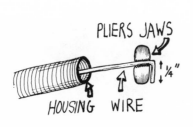

PLIERS JAWS

HOUSING WIRE

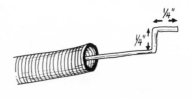

Illustration **30a**
Control Wire "Z" Bend

up so that about 4 or 5 inches are sticking out the lever
end. Make the Z bend right at the very tip of the wire.
Either work it into the hole in the lever, or, if it's easier,
unbolt (c-cl) the lever and wiggle it onto the Z. Whichever
you do, tighten (cl) the lever bolt after the wire is attached.
Often a loose lever bolt caused the wire breakage in the
first place. If your lever is just crimped on and you can't
tighten it, get a whole new lever. When the wire is firmly
attached in the lever, try moving the lever back and forth
a few times (see illustration 30b). The other end of the
wire down by the clutch mechanism should shoot in and
out of the housing nicely. If the housing is loose in the
clamp screw, just hold the housing with your hand and
try the lever out. Make sure it is working right before you
connect the clutch mechanism end of the wire.

Fiddle with the mechanism (moving it back and
forth with your bare hands) as well, to find out which
position the clutch naturally rests in, engaged, or disengaged (if it'll stay put in any position, put it at one
extreme or the other, and leave it there), and which
position of the control lever this corresponds to. If there
are little words, like "Stop" and "Go" printed on the
control level panel, that makes it easy. "Stop" will cor-
respond to a disengaged clutch mechanism, "Go" to an
engaged clutch. But if there aren't any of those handy
marks, or if the marks have worn away, first you have to
put the mechanism in the position it naturally rests in,
and then make sure that you have the lever set at the

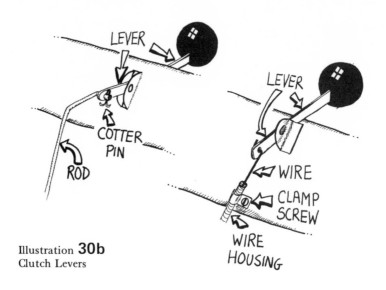

Illustration **30b**
Clutch Levers

proper extreme so that when the connected wire is moved,
the lever will either pull or push the mechanism to its
opposite extreme. This may be a bit hard to visualize.
To clarify it to yourself, get a friend to move the clutch
mechanism while you move the lever. Watch the wire as
it shoots in and out of the clutch end of the housing,
and work the clutch mechanism so it parallels the motion
of the wire end. Got it all straightened out in your mind?
Good. Now set the mechanism at the extreme where it
naturally rests, and put the lever at the corresponding
extreme. Loosen the clamp screw that holds the mechanism end of the wire housing. Slide the housing back and
forth until it is in such a position that it can be moved
an inch either way to adjust the wire length without either
tightening up so you can't raise the mower handle, or getting so loose that it catches on things and gets in your
way. (Your housing won't fit in that range no matter how
much you slide it around? Get a longer or cut a shorter
housing, as needed.) Snug up (cl) the clamp screw just
enough so the housing stays put.

Find the point on the wire where it passes over the
cable hole in the clutch mechanism. Pinch that point with

the fingers of one hand. With the other hand (and a screw-driver, natch), loosen (c-cl) the clamp screw and pull the end of the housing and the wire back out and away from the mower where you can work on them. Cut off the wire about ½ inch beyond where you are pinching it. Then grab the last ¼ inch of the wire with your needlenose pliers and make a bend down. Make the second bend of the Z by grabbing the next ¼ inch of the wire and bending up, as shown in illustration 30a. Beware, however. On some rare mowers, the dimensions of the Z bend have to be a little different. If the Z you just made doesn't fit your clutch mechanism because yours has a thick pole or a very narrow space that the Z has to fit through, then make a new Z as needed.

When you have a Z that fits, curve the wire and housing around so the end of the wire will go into its hole. If there isn't enough extra cable and housing to allow this, don't try stretching or yanking the wire; you'll just kink it or the housing or both so they won't work. Move either the lever or the mechanism to give yourself a little more free room, then guide the wire end into its hole using the needlenose pliers.

When the end of the wire is in place, put the housing back under the clamp screw. Don't tighten the screw yet. But check to make sure the housing is in place and firmly held at the lever end (if there is a clamp screw at the lever end, tighten (cl) it well). Then put the lever in the extreme position that pulls the wire out as far as possible at the lever end. The position that leaves the least amount of wire showing at the clutch mechanism end, in other words.

Finally, grasp the clutch mechanism end of the housing, and pull it so that it slides under the clamp screw as far as it will go toward the lever. Then tighten (cl) the clamp screw. This will fix the whole system in a tightened position. The clamp screw tightening (cl) will be easy if the clutch rests naturally with the lever in the position you now have it. But if the clutch rests naturally at the other extreme, you will have to pull hard on that housing to get things tightened up. Don't twist too hard on the clamp screw in the excitement; it's all too easy to strip the threads or tighten the clamp so much that it mashes the housing down on the wire.

Try out the clutch. If the system works, you're on easy street. If the clutch still won't completely engage or disengage, first see if the wire is allowing the clutch mechanism to move from one extreme of its range to the other. The wire might be so tight that it doesn't let the mechanism out enough. In that case, loosen (c-cl) the clamp screw and let the housing slip under about ¼ inch toward the mechanism. Tighten (cl) the clamp screw, and try the system out again. If the wire *is* moving the mechanism through its entire range of motion, but the damn thing just ain't tightening or loosening up enough, so the mower still either won't get its ass into gear, or won't stop when you tell it to, then go to the *Clutch Mechanism Adjustment* (page 102).

WIRE OR ROD ADJUSTMENT

There are two different ways that the clutch can get out of adjustment. Either the control lever can't even move from one extreme of its range to the other, or the lever can move, but the mechanism does not move far enough in its range to fully engage or disengage the clutch.

Check the lever first. If the lever can move all the way from one extreme to the other, the mechanism may need some work. See the *Mechanism Adjustment* section below. If the lever *can't* move through all of its range, the rod or wire must be out of adjustment. For a wire that's too tight or loose to allow full use of the lever, loosen (c-cl) the housing clamp screw at the mechanism end of the wire. Slide the housing under the clamp screw, about ¼ inch either way, so that the lever can do its thing the way it should from one extreme to the other. Tighten (cl) the clamp screw, and try the clutch again. Still not making it into or out of gear? See *Mechanism Adjustment,* below.

On a rod-controlled clutch, look for a threaded sleeve and locknut at the mechanism end of the rod. Loosen (c-cl) the locknut. To turn the sleeve may require unhooking it from the mechanism. When the sleeve is free to turn, either shorten the rod by turning the sleeve counterclockwise, or lengthen the rod with a couple of clockwise turns. Try the clutch out to make sure you have moved the thing the right way before you tighten (cl) the locknut. If you find that even when the lever can move from one extreme to the other, the clutch still won't get the mower completely into or out of gear, go on to the *Mechanism Adjustment* (page 102).

Chain

Description

The chain takes the power from the clutch mechanism to the reel. It runs on a small sprocket up at the clutch, and a much larger sprocket down on the reel. This makes the reel turn at about a quarter to a half the speed of the mower engine. There is a master link in the chain which allows you to take it apart and remove it (see illustration 31). There are three common sizes of chain, and some foreign chains that come in oddball sizes, so you have to match an old chain with any new replacement one to make sure you're getting the right size.

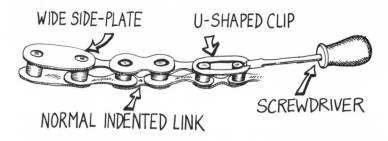

WIDE SIDE-PLATE   U-SHAPED CLIP

NORMAL INDENTED LINK   SCREWDRIVER

Illustration **31**
Chain Links

Problems

CHAIN THROWN OFF SPROCKETS

Your mower went over a particularly bad bump (damn gophers anyway; make a lawn look like the Swiss Alps), or maybe the clutch got a little cranky and jerky, and the chain flopped right off the sprockets.

First undo and ground the spark plug wire so you can't get made into mincemeat while working down around the reel blades (see Frontispiece). After disarming the mower, remove (c-cl) any screws holding down shields over the chain. You can put the shields down on the floor upside down and leave the screws in them so you don't lose any. Then move the clutch lever back and forth, and watch the small sprocket that is attached to the mechanism. Does the sprocket move when the clutch moves? On some clutches, like the dead-man type (see illustration 29a), the whole clutch shaft moves when you move the handle to engage and disengage the clutch. If your setup is like that, put the clutch in the disengaged position (so the belt is loose). This would make the chain looser, if the chain was still in place. It will therefore make the setting of the chain easier, because you won't have to pull the chain so tight. For those of you who can't move your clutch sprocket, don't worry, you'll be able to replace your chain, too, if you use some tricks.

Before you put the chain back on the sprockets, you have to undo the master link. Finding the master link can be a long, messy process. If the chain has fallen under the mower deck, pull a loop of it back up topside. Look for a side-plate with no indentations, or the little U-shaped clip over the ends of the rivers, as in illustration 31. When you find the master link, brush the gunk off it with your wire brush.

To get the U-shaped clip type undone, stick a corner of a screwdriver blade against the ends of the arms of the U; push and wiggle the screwdriver so that the ends of the U arms spread apart and slide around the rivet (see illustration 31). When the clip has slipped off one rivet, you can

90

wiggle and twist it off the other one with your bare hands. If you happen to mangle or bend the thing in the process, don't worry, you can get a replacement at any mower shop; just remember to take the old one with you so you get the same size. Once you have the U clip off, you can slide the whole link out of the chain, but *hold on* to *both* ends of the chain so neither one falls down under the deck.

To undo the wide side-plate link, grasp the chain firmly (yech!), one hand just to each side of the master link. Hold the chain so that the wide, un-indented side-plate is facing you, then use your hands to flex the chain so the master link bends away from you (as if you are trying to break a twig for firewood). As the chain flexes sideways, the rivets of the master link will point more toward each other. That will loosen the wide side-plate. Usually, it will just fall off, or you can shake it off by moving the whole chain around a bit. But if the link is so gunky that it won't come off without a little encouragement, have a friend stick a small screwdriver under the plate and pry it off as you hold the chain bent. Once you have the wide side-plate off, you can let the chain loose again and pull the rest of the master link out. But *hold on* to *both* ends of the chain. If you lose one end or the other down under the reel, the chain will be that much harder to reconnect.

SETTING THE CHAIN

While still holding both ends of the chain firmly, and keeping them above the deck, check to see if the chain is off both sprockets. Chain still on the big sprocket? Fine—skip the next paragraph and go on.

Chain off both sprockets? See if you can loop the lower part of the chain under and back onto the points of the reel sprocket. No go? That's often the case. Hold onto the end of the chain that's toward the front of the deck, and let the other end of the chain fall down under the deck. Grab it down there, reaching from behind the mower, and try to loop the chain onto the points of the reel sprocket from that vantage point. If that is to no avail, pull the end of the chain that's below the deck as far back as you can without letting go of the other end. Set a couple of links of the chain over the bottom points of the reel sprocket, and start pulling the chain from its top end, so that it threads on from the bottom. When the threaded-on section of the chain has extended all the way under the sprocket, look down from above the deck, through the forward part of the chain hole. Thread the chain on a little farther, until you can see the threaded-on portion come around. Now nudge the mower forward with your shoulder and thread the chain from top to bottom to get it evened up again, so both ends are up in the vicinity of the small upper clutch sprocket. You may need to have a friend hold the front-most end of the chain while you pass the rear end back up through the hole in the deck. Just don't let loose of the front-most end so that it falls down into the works where you can't reach it.

Set the ends of the chain between two adjacent points of the small clutch sprocket (see illustration 32). This may take some grunting and stretching. What's that? You dropped the front end of the chain down through the deck, didn't you? Call the thing by a properly nasty name or two, and go to the second half of the *Chain Exchange* procedure for hints on how to rethread the thing.

When the chain is set so the ends are between adjacent points on the clutch sprocket, plug the master link

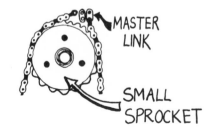

Illustration **32**
Setting the Chain

into the two end holes. Push either the wide side-plate or the regular side-plate and the little U clip into place on the end of the master link rivets. You should be able to do this with your bare fingers, but use the needlenose pliers if you need a little leverage. Squeeze the link together slowly and gently, working it into place a bit at a time, so you don't mash or bend it out of shape. If the link gets bent in spite of, or because of, your best efforts, take it to a shop and replace it. Don't leave a bent link to hold the chain together. You know what they always say about the weakest one.

With the master link all together, you can try the thing out. Engage the clutch and pull the starter without hooking the spark plug wire back up. The mower should move forward and the chain should glide freely on the sprockets. If the chain is a bit uneven, see *Chain Jerky*, below. If the chain is loose even with the clutch mechanism engaged, then the chain needs tightening; loose chains throw easily. See *Chain Adjustment* under *Clutch Mechanism* on page 98; (I know it seems illogical to have the chain adjustment under the clutch mechanism heading, but believe me, lawnmowers generate a logic all their own). If the chain seems tight and oiled OK, but still throws, undo it and go on to the *Chain Exchange*. If the whole system works now, that's great. Replace any shields you took off, screw the screws back in (cl), reconnect the spark plug wire, and you're set to go. Wash up thoroughly after doing this job, especially if you're about to go into the kitchen for a snack.

CHAIN JERKY
The chain makes all kinds of grindy, clanky noises, and jerks the mower along unevenly (there's no reference to beef jerky intended, so don't try chewing the chain—chewing won't help it at all). Undo the spark plug wire and ground it before you start messing around, then remove any shields that prevent you from getting at the chain above the deck. Put the clutch in gear, grab the

chain between the sprockets, and pull on it. Is it so loose that you can stretch it ½ inch out of the direct line between the sprockets? If it is, see *Chain Adjustment* under *Mechanism Problems.* If the chain isn't loose, but is very dry or even rusty, take the clutch out of gear and turn the reel backwards by hand from in front of the mower, like in illustration 10, so that the chain moves slowly over the clutch sprocket (the little one on top). Drip motor oil on the rollers all the way around. Back the mower around a bit so that the reel spins and oil gets worked in, then wipe any great globs of extra oil off the chain. If the jerkiness persists even after oil has gotten worked in, the chain is probably shot—go to the *Chain Exchange.* But if the chain now runs smoothly on the sprockets, replace the shields you took off and tighten (cl) the screws for holding them. The chain should run quietly now, and last longer, too.

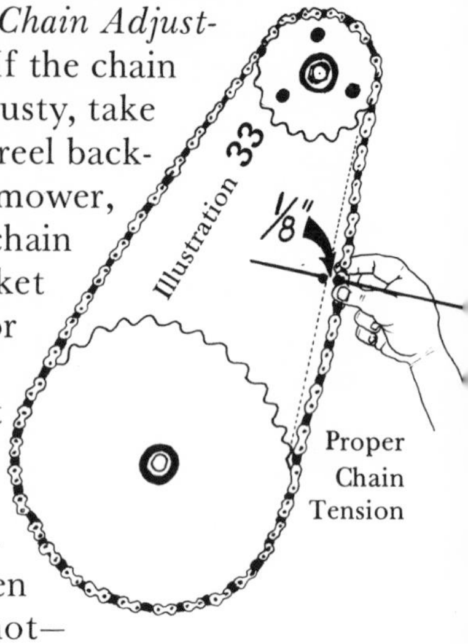

Illustration 33

⅛"

Proper
Chain
Tension

CHAIN SHOT
You have been directed here from other sections, or you can see for yourself that your chain is bent, broken, or stretched to the point where it no longer runs smoothly over the sprockets.

CHAIN EXCHANGE
First undo and ground the spark plug wire on the engine and remove any shields that are between you and the chain. Any screws you took out (c-cl) to get the shields off you can put in the upturned shields for safekeeping. If the chain is broken simply disentangle it from the works (watch your fingers around the blades) and pull it off the sprockets. If the chain is still connected, find the master link as in illustration 31 and undo it. If you need some

hints on the undoing, see the third paragraph of the *Chain Thrown Off Sprockets* procedure.

Take the chain you have removed and go with it in hand (yech—maybe in a *rag* in hand) to a good mower shop. Get a replacement chain that is the same size side-to-side, and that has the same pitch (distance between the centers of any two rollers). When you compare your old shot chain with a new one, remember that the old chain is stretched out. You want a new chain that has the same number of links as the old one, but that is un-stretched, and therefore slightly shorter. Lay the old chain and the new chain down on your rag on the counter at the mower shop, right next to each other so you can compare their lengths and numbers of links. The guy in the shop can help you make sure you get exactly the right replacement chain.

Take your nice clean new chain and put it in a clean place while you get ready to mount it on the mower. Block the front of the mower up off the ground as in illustration 22.

Check to make sure you can turn the reel both ways easily. Watch your fingers. Disengage the clutch, especially if this normally loosens the chain, as on the dead-man type unit (see illustration 29a). Remove the master link from the chain, if it isn't already separated. Hold one end of the chain, and lower the other end down through the front part of the chain slot in the deck. Start the first two or three links of the chain onto the reel sprocket down there, holding the chain in a straight line going up from the sprocket. When the chain has started to feed onto the sprocket, turn the reel blades with one hand, still holding the end of the chain up in the air and lowering it as the chain feeds down around the reel sprocket.

Watch for the chain to appear below the sprocket. On mowers with a shield around the sprocket, you have to look from behind the mower. On machines that have no shield down there, the chain will be visible from the front of the mower. Try to reach the chain with your fingers, or if they are too short, use the needlenose pliers. Get a good hold on the lower end of the chain and pass it toward the back of the mower over the cutter bar. Keep a good hold on the end of the chain that's above the deck, too, or even have a friend hold that end, so you don't drop the whole thing down through the deck. It will take some fiddling and finagling around, especially on the models that have a shield under the sprocket, limiting your working space. Don't worry if the chain gets folded down in there, as long as it doesn't jam or throw the part you already threaded off the sprocket. When you have the lower end of the chain out the back over the cutter bar, hold both ends of the chain with your hands and run it back and forth on the reel sprocket to make sure it's on there good. Then pass the end that's now toward the back of the mower up through the back of the chain hole in the deck, and grab it from topside. This process may take three hands, too, so get a friend to lend one if you need it.

Stretch the chain tight and try to put the ends over the clutch sprocket so that the end rollers are between adjacent points on the sprocket. Too tight? That's often the case (if that isn't the case, and the end links *do* fit between adjacent points on the sprocket, just skip the next two paragraphs and go on).

Take the ends of the chain off the sprocket and link them together with the master link. You don't have to put the U clip or wide side-plate on, just push the rivets through the end rollers and stick a screwdriver under the loop of chain so it won't fall back under the deck.

Loosen (c-cl) the clutch mounting bolts (see illustration 29a, b, c, d) and move the clutch mechanism forward or down so it will make more room for the new, shorter chain length. Go to *Chain Adjustment* (page 98) under *Clutch Mechanism Problems* if you need hints on how to move the mechanism around. But don't forget to come back here when the clutch mechanism is loose so you can put the chain on, then go back there for the final adjustment of your new chain.

Got that clutch mechanism loose and moved down or forward? Good. Now take the master link out of the ends of the chain and set the ends between adjacent points on the sprocket (see illustration 32). Hold the ends in place with one hand and slip the rivets of the master link through the end rollers with the other hand. Pinch on the wide side-plate using pliers, or spread, wiggle and slide the U clip into place using a screwdriver blade. Take care with either type of master link—they don't work when they're bent.

Make sure you undid and grounded the spark plug wire before, leave the clutch disengaged, and turn the mower wheels backwards to check whether the chain works. It might well be too loose now. If it is, go to the *Chain Adjustment* (page 98) under *Clutch Mechanism Problems*. If the chain is in adjustment, that is to say, if you can grab it at the midpoint between the sprockets and move it about 1/8 inch toward and away from the midline between the sprocket axles (see illustration 33), then tighten any clutch mechanism mounting bolts you loosened and try out the clutch. Clutch loose now? Might have guessed it'd do a thing like that. Go to the *Clutch Mechanism Adjustment* procedure below. If the clutch and chain both work OK, then you can replace the shields if there were any, screw in (cl) the screws, hook the spark plug wire back up, and mow away. Your chain and clutch shouldn't give you any trouble for a long time.

Clutch Mechanism

Description

The clutch mechanism is the unit which actually moves a belt or cone into and out of contact with the spinning engine shaft, thus stopping and starting the spinning of the chain, reel and wheels of the mower. There are two basic clutch designs in common use. One design has a black rubber belt running on pulleys (see illustration 29a, b, d). The other design has a cone and cup assembly which fits directly around the engine shaft (see illustration 29c). The pulley design clutches can be subdivided into models with two pulleys with movable jackshafts (see illustration 29a), models with two regular pulleys and an idler pulley that stretches and loosens the drive belt (see illustration 29b), and models with a pulley that pinches the belt or widens to release it (see illustration 29d).

Problems

CLUTCH TOO LOOSE OR TIGHT

Either the clutch won't disengage, and the mower runs all over the place the minute you pull the starter, or the clutch won't engage, and you can't get the mower to move no matter how much you twiddle with the lever. Have you checked that lever? If not, see the *Control Lever and Linkage* section (page 81).

If you have narrowed down the problem to the clutch mechanism itself, you might think that the logical way to proceed is to loosen the clutch mechanism mounting bolts, and slide the clutch around until it works. Lawnmower logic is never so simple. Moving the clutch mechanism adjusts the chain, odd as that might seem. The way to adjust the clutch is to move the engine, on all models but the cone clutch one (illustration 29c). The whole clutch system is adjusted by first adjusting the chain tension (i.e., moving the clutch mechanism), and second adjusting the engine position. Always do it in that order. If your chain is adjusted properly (see illustration 33), all you have to do is move the engine to get your clutch right. But if both the chain and clutch are out of whack, first do the

CHAIN ADJUSTMENT

Start by undoing and grounding the spark plug wire (see Frontispiece). Take off any shields covering the clutch mechanism and upper part of the chain, unscrewing (c-cl) the screws, then turning the shields upside down and putting the screws in them so you don't lose any.

Decide which mechanism in illustration 29a, b, c, d is closest to being like yours, then find the mounting bolts that hold the clutch mechanism to the rest of the mower. (What's that? Your mower has a completely different clutch mounting than the illustrated ones? That's OK if it's a Jacobsen mower; on those you simply find those big bolts through the deck at the right and left rear corners, then turn the nuts on top of the deck counterclockwise a full turn or so, pry the deck up with the big screwdriver until you only have about 1/8 inch slack in the chain as in illustration 33, then turn the lower nuts up (c-cl) by hand until they are snug against the underside of the deck, and finally tighten (cl) the upper nuts down on the deck with a wrench—lucky you, if your clutch was OK you don't have to do a clutch adjustment after tightening your chain, as everyone else does.) Look closely at the holes that the bolts go through. If the holes are hidden by the bottom plate of the mechanism, feel around under the mower deck (scrape off the dirt under there with a screwdriver, and watch that you don't cut your fingers on the blades) and find out what shape the mounting bolt holes are.

If the mounting bolt holes are long slots, you will be able to loosen the bolts and move the mechanism around to tighten or loosen the chain. If the holes are just little round ones (you won't be able to see or feel the holes because they will be filled with bolts and covered by the bolt heads and the nuts) you will tighten the chain by loosening the mounting bolts and placing shims (as in illustration 29d) between the bottom plate of the mechanism and the deck of the mower. Figured out which mounting bolt setup you have? Fine—go on to the appropriate paragraph below.

People with *slotted holes for the mounting bolts* (illustration 29a, b, c), start by engaging and disengaging the clutch, to see if that tightens or loosens the chain. If your clutch has a movable jackshaft, like the dead-man type (illustration 29a), you will notice that the chain goes slack when the clutch is disengaged. Remember this as you tighten the chain by moving the mechanism. You don't want to have the chain so tight that when you engage the clutch, it snaps. Whatever your mechanism looks like, loosen (c-cl) all of the mounting bolts that hold it in place by at least a full turn. When the mechanism is free to slide around, move it either back on the deck (as in illustration 29a, b) or up on the bracket (29c). Move it about ¼ inch, no more. Tighten (cl) the mounting bolts just enough to keep the mechanism in place for the moment, and check to see how tight the chain is. You want the chain, at its tightest (on the 29a types, this means with the clutch engaged) to have about 1/8 inch slack. If you grab the chain at a point between the sprockets, you should be able to move it only 1/8 inch toward and away from an imaginary line running between the centers of the sprocket axles (see illustration 33). Never, but NEVER should the chain be so tight that when you pull it and let it go it quivers like a banjo string. An overtight chain will do its damndest to pull the sprockets closer together, especially under load. It'll pull until it breaks, or until the bearings on the clutch and reel (heaven forbid!) are worn to hell, or until all the points are worn right off the sprocket. Bad news in any case. So move your clutch mechanism several times if you have to, to make sure you have the old 1/8 inch of slack. If the chain is too loose to be tightened even if you move the clutch mechanism all the way back, you need a new chain—go to *Chain Exchange.* But if your chain is OK, get the slack just right as described. Then make sure the mechanism is still aligned by using a straight edge as in illustration 34, or sighting from above the jackshaft and lining it up with the trailing edge of the mower deck. When the chain and the mechanism are aligned, tighten (cl) the mounting bolts thoroughly. Give the chain a final check for the 1/8 inch of slack with the clutch both engaged and disengaged, then go on to the *Clutch Mechanism Adjustment* below. If you have a setup like illustration 29c, and your clutch is OK, you don't have to adjust the clutch, you lucky dog.

For those of you who have clutch mechanisms with little *round mounting bolt holes* (illustration 29d), loosen (c-cl) the mounting bolts about two full turns apiece. To raise the position of the mechanism and tighten the chain, you are going to simply pull the mechanism up and stick something under it to make it stay at its raised level. Special shims for the purpose are often supplied with the mower. What's that? You couldn't figure out what those little ⌶◡‾◡⌷ shaped pieces of metal were? I bet you threw them away or lost them. Or maybe, like me, you never throw little oddities like that away, but always put them in some obscure box or drawer where you can never find them again. Don't sweat it if you have lost the shims one way or the other. First call the shop where you got the mower, tell them the model number of your mower (it'll be stamped on the identification plate) and ask them if they have the shims for your model. If they do, get a bunch, like four. If they don't, or if you got the mower second hand and don't have a handy shop to rely on, there's another solution. Get some plumber's metal tape, the kind with all the holes in it, then either buy or borrow a pair of tin snips and cut U-shaped slots into the tape so it will make a good shim to slide under the mechanism around the mounting bolts. Shim up the mechanism with two shims at a time, one each on the front and the back of the mechanism. After you put each pair of shims in, tighten (cl) the mounting bolts completely, and check the chain for the 1/8 inch slack as in illustration 33. Make sure you don't tighten the chain to the point that it quivers like a banjo string if you pull it and let go. An overtight chain can destroy the whole mower.

When the chain is adjusted, check to make sure the mechanism is still straight. Put a straightedge against the sides of the pulleys to see if they're in line (see illustration 34), or sight along some straight horizontal line on the mechanism, like the jackshaft housing, and see if it lines up with the trailing edge of the mower deck. Loosen (c-cl) the mounting bolts and twist the mechanism until it's straight. Chain tight and mechanism aligned? Tighten (cl) the mechanism mounting bolts well, and go right on to

CLUTCH MECHANISM ADJUSTMENT

Your mower won't obey you. It goes when you want it to stand still, or it lingers and stops when you want it to keep going. First, check the preliminaries of clutch adjustment. Have you unhooked and grounded the spark plug wire? Have you removed any shields over the clutch? How about the chain adjustment, and the lever and linkage; are they all in order? Have you checked the belt, to make sure it isn't shot? If you have done all these things, and the old clutch is still out of whack, then you're in the right department. Each type of clutch requires a different sort of adjustment procedure. Look closely at your clutch mechanism and compare it to those in illustration 29a, b, c, d.

The *Dead-Man Clutch Adjustment* (29a) can be done two ways. If the clutch is only slightly out of adjustment, you can use a simple adjusting screw to get it back in working shape. Look for the adjusting screw either where the handle hits the dead-man lever, or at the other end of that same lever (see illustration 29a).

On the type where the handle hits the adjusting screw, loosen the two locknuts (top c-cl, bottom cl) and turn the screw counterclockwise to make the clutch disengage quicker, or clockwise to make the clutch engage more easily. Lock the nuts (top cl, bottom c-cl). If the mechanism needs more adjusting, or if you have to put the handle way too low or too high to work the clutch, skip the next paragraph and go on to the major adjustment procedure.

On the type where the adjusting screw sticks out the back of the mechanism (not illustrated), loosen (c-cl) the single locknut, and turn the screw clockwise to make the clutch disengage more quickly, or counterclockwise to make the clutch engage sooner. If more than a minor adjustment is needed, go on to the next paragraph.

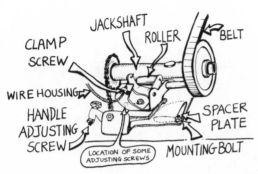

Illustration **29a** (repeated)
Dead Man Clutch

If major adjustment is needed, lock the handle of the mower in its vertical position so it can't put the clutch on by accident. On the models with the wire and lever control (like in illustration 29a), put the lever in the "Go" or "Ease-O-Matic" position. Loosen (c-cl) the bolts that hold the engine to the deck. Move the engine a smidgen at a time, either forward or back on the deck, until the roller of the clutch mechanism is just barely touching the jackshaft housing. On the models which have this roller out in the open, there is a spacer plate at the right rear corner of the clutch mechanism that helps you get the roller-barely-touching adjustment. Loosen (c-cl) the bolt holding the spacer plate, slide the plate under the mechanism, and press down on the mechanism as you budge the engine back and forth. Tighten (cl) the engine bolts when the roller is just touching the shaft housing. Then slide the spacer plate back out, and tighten (cl) its mounting bolt. On other models, you can't see the roller to find out when it's barely touching. Just twiddle the lever that the handle hits before and after each slight move of the engine. When the jackshaft housing moves off the roller in there, you'll feel the lever move the roller over that extra space in there. Move the engine back just a hair so that there is no longer any extra space if you twiddle the lever, then tighten up (cl) the engine mounting bolts.

Whichever model you have, check the pulley alignment as in illustration 34, or check for the back edge of
the engine block being parallel with the rear edge of the
deck. If the engine is out of alignment, loosen the mounting bolts, twist the engine very slightly without moving it
and upsetting the clutch adjustment. Tighten the engine
mounting bolts thoroughly when you have both the
adjustment and the alignment right. Try the clutch out,
just pulling the starter cord to see if the engine turns the
reel and wheels. If the clutch needs minor adjustment,
do it with the adjusting screw. Clutch OK now? Good.
Replace any shields you took off and screw the screws
back in (cl), hook the spark plug wire up again, and you're
set to go.

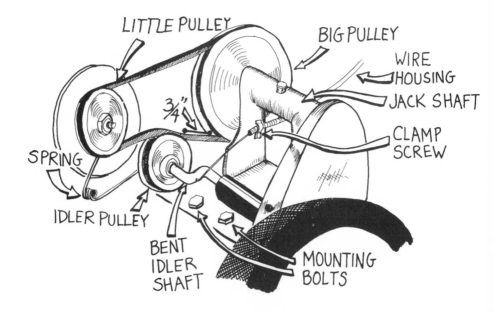

Illustration **29b** (repeated)
Idler Pulley Clutch

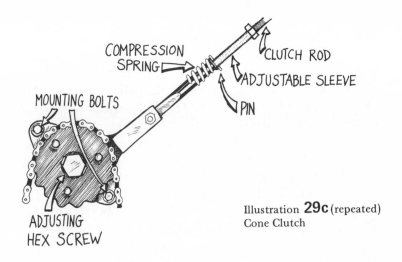

COMPRESSION
SPRING

CLUTCH ROD

ADJUSTABLE SLEEVE

PIN

MOUNTING BOLTS

ADJUSTING
HEX SCREW

Illustration **29c** (repeated)
Cone Clutch

Adjustment of the *Bent Idler Shaft* type mechanism (illustration 29b) is very simple. Loosen the engine mounting bolts and slide the engine either ¼ inch forward to lighten the clutch belt, or ¼ inch back to loosen it. The idea is to get the belt tight enough so that when the clutch is engaged, the idler pushes against the tight belt with about ¾ inch of belt between the idler and the big pulley (see illustration 29b). If the wire is holding things up so you can't move the engine, loosen (c-cl) the housing clamp screw. Check the pulley alignment as in illustration 34 when you think the belt is the right tightness. Twist the engine in place if you have to in order to get the pulleys lined up, then tighten (cl) the engine mounting bolts. Try engaging and disengaging the clutch. Pull the starter rope with the clutch on and off to check whether the thing is working. The wire may need adjustment. If so, see the *Wire or Rod Adjustment* procedure in the *Clutch Control Lever and Linkage* section (page 88). Clutch snapping into and out of gear now? If it's still sluggish, it may be that the spring is old and weary. Go to *Spring Shot,* below. If the clutch is snappy, that's fine. Replace the shield you took off, screw in (cl) the screws, reconnect the spark plug wire, and you're set to go.

The *Cone* clutch (see illustration 29c) adjustment is rarely needed. If the clutch slips after long usage, tighten it up by prying the lock tabs away from the adjusting hex screw at the sprocket end of the clutch mechanism. Tighten (cl) the screw 1/6 of a turn and bend one of the lock tabs back into place so the screw can't turn. Test the clutch by pulling the starter rope. If it needs to be tighter, loosen the tab again and take another 1/6 turn (cl) on the adjusting screw. When the clutch works without slipping, bend both lock tabs around the adjusting screw. Replace the shield, screw in (cl) the screws, hook the spark plug wire back on, and you're all set.

The *Pinch-Pulley* type clutch (illustration 29d) is adjusted with the mechanism engaged. Loosen (c-cl) the engine mounting bolts and move the engine ¼ inch forward to tighten or ¼ inch backward to loosen the clutch. Tighten the mounting bolts just enough to keep the engine put for the moment. Pull the starter rope. If the clutch belt is tight enough, there will be an audible click as the clutch engages the big pulley and the jackshaft. Disengage the clutch and make sure the starter rope doesn't still engage the mechanism. If it does, loosen the engine bolts again and find the happy median position for the engine by moving it back and forth a smidgen at a time. When the system works, leave it in the engaged position and check for pulley alignment as in illustration 34. Loosen the engine mounting bolts yet again and twist the engine in place if it has gotten out of alignment. Engine aligned and adjusted? Great. Replace the shield if you took it off, reconnect the spark plug wire, and you can start using the mower confidently again, knowing it won't take off the moment you start it, or slip its gears every time you come to a little hill or a clump of thick grass.

CLUTCH SLUGGISH

You have adjusted the clutch control, the chain, and the mechanism, and the clutch works, but is very sluggish, or jams in one position or the other. Undo the spark plug

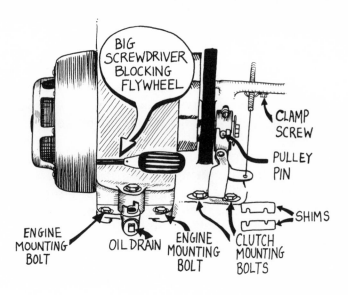

Illustration **29d** (repeated)
Pinch-Pulley Clutch

wire and ground it (see Frontispiece), and take off any
shields over the clutch if you haven't already. Try moving
the mechanism in and out of the engaged position with
your bare hands. Watch the clutch spring and the parts
of the mechanism that turn on each other as you do so.

If the whole mechanism is obviously bent or broken
in some way, then you have to replace it. Remove the
chain as in *Chain Shot* (page 94), and take the belt
off as per *Belt Shot,* below. Undo the control linkage,
either unhooking or unscrewing (c-cl) the end of the rod,
or unscrewing (c-cl) the clamp screw and taking the wire
out of its hole. Loosen (c-cl) the clutch mechanism mounting bolts and remove them. Take the whole mechanism
down to a mower shop that deals in the kind of mower
you have, and get a replacement. Don't be surprised if
you have to wait while they order a new one.

If the mechanism isn't obviously discombobulated,
check the spring. Is it broken? Or is it old and tired, so
that the mechanism slogs listlessly from position to position? Go right on to——

SPRING SHOT

Before pulling the spring off, set the clutch mechanism in the position that lets the spring go loosest. If the spring is out in the open and easy to remove, as shown in illustration 29b, grab the most easily accessible end of the spring and undo it. Use pliers for a good grip, and watch out that the end of the spring doesn't jump out and take a bite at your fingers. Take the spring to your friendly mower shop and get an exact replacement; don't accept a reasonable facsimile, get the same type of spring. You'll probably have to wait while they order one. Place the least accessible end of the new spring first, then grab the other end firmly with a pair of pliers and stretch it into place. If the spring on your mower is obviously a very awkward one to get at like the one on the dead-man clutch (illustration 29a), don't drive yourself crazy trying to get it out and replace it. Have the job done by a mower shop that handles that model mower. They'll have special tools and know-how for the job.

BELT SHOT, OR CLUTCH JAMMED

Either your belt has worn all the way down and broken, or you left the clutch engaged by mistake, and the belt got deformed so that it jumps and jams when you engage the clutch. If the belt is broken, it's pretty easy to get it off the pulleys. But if the belt isn't broken, you have to move the pulleys close together and slip the belt over them and off. Unbolt (c-cl) and remove any shields over the belt that are in your way. Some mowers have shields that are stuck around the pulleys so you can't get them off—very poor design! On these mowers you have to work around the shields.

Try loosening the belt by just disengaging the clutch. If you're lucky, that'll make the belt loose enough to slip off the pulleys. In many cases, the belt will come off the little pulley more easily that it'll come off the big one. Try shoe-horning the thing off with a screwdriver. But go easily; the pulleys are made of cheap metal and are thus fragile. If disengaging the clutch doesn't loosen the belt enough so you can get if off (this will certainly be the case on the Pinch-pulley models as in illustration 29d), you have to resort to loosening (c-cl) the engine mounting bolts, and moving the whole engine back on the deck to loosen the belt. If this also fails (it will, again, on the Pinch-pulley type), you must remove one of the pulleys altogether. Look closely at the little pulley. On the shoulder of this pulley (the wide part that is around the engine shaft, there may be a little bolt set in, with a hexagon-shaped hole in it. This is a hex set screw (see illustration 34). If both pulleys have them, the pulley on the engine shaft will be easier to work on, so loosen the screw on it with an allen wrench (Pinch-pulley people—once again, you miss out; your little pulley is much more complicated, so you have to skip down to the paragraph on you below). See if you can wiggle and pull the pulley off, maybe tapping it lightly with a hammer for encouragement. Often it will be fit tightly over a little half-circle key called a woodruff key. If your pulley won't come off with a little encouragement, don't do anything rash like prying it or whacking it with a hammer to try to get it off. Either get a gear and pulley puller (see *Tools* in Appendix), or take the mower to a shop and have them use their special puller to get the pulley off and replace the belt. If the pulley does come off easily for you, be careful you don't lose the woodruff key.

When you have your belt off one way or the other, take the old one to a shop and get an exact replacement. Put your nice new belt over the pulleys. If you didn't have to take the little pulley off, you can replace any shields you took off, tighten (cl) the screws, hook up the spark plug wire, and mow away.

To replace a little pulley, turn the engine shaft so that the slot in it for the woodruff key is up. That way the woodruff key will sit in there while you line up the key slot in the pulley and slide the pulley into place. When the thing is on snug, see if it is lined up as in illustration 34. Jiggle it around if you have to, or even loosen (c-cl) the engine mounting bolts to get things lined up, then tighten (cl) the hex set screw with the allen wrench. Check the clutch operation out when everything is set. If the clutch has been messed up by putting on a new, tight belt, see the *Clutch Mechanism Adjustment* above. When you've done all necessary adjusting and aligning, replace any shields you took off, screw in (cl) the screws, reconnect the spark plug wire, and you're set to mow.

People with the Pinch-pulley system, you have a more complicated job of removing the little pulley to get the belt off. Start by sticking the blade of a big screwdriver across the front of the mower and under the blower housing so that it will block the flywheel and thus keep the engine shaft from turning the way it turns when the engine is on (see illustration 29d). With the shaft thus blocked, loosen (c-cl) the bolt that sticks out of the pulley end of the shaft, and remove the bolt and the washers under it. Then pry the small y of the clutch yoke off the pin on the front of the movable half of the pulley. Wiggle the back arm of the yoke over the pin on that side of the pulley, and slide the movable side of the pulley right off the end of the shaft. Pull the belt first off the little pulley shaft and then off the big pulley. Get an exact replacement belt and put it in place. Put the movable half of the little pulley back into position on its yoke, making sure that the y arm of the yoke is to the front, and move the clutch mechanism by hand so that the movable half of the pulley slides back over the shaft. Squeeze the yoke arms in on the pulley pins with the channel lock pliers. Replace first the springy washer, then any solid washers, and finally the bolt on the end of the shaft. Tighten (cl) the bolt, holding the shaft still with the big screwdriver in the flywheel again. If the new belt has put the control lever out of adjustment, set the clutch in its engaged or belt-pinching position, and put the lever in the "go" position. Slide the wire housing under the clamp screw (you have to loosen the screw, if you haven't already) as far

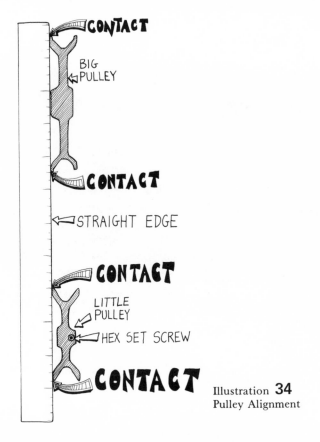

CONTACT

BIG PULLEY

CONTACT

STRAIGHT EDGE

CONTACT

LITTLE PULLEY

HEX SET SCREW

CONTACT

Illustration **34**
Pulley Alignment

toward the back of the mower as you can. Tighten (cl) the screw, and try out the clutch by pulling the starter cord. If the new belt won't quite disengage, loosen the engine mounting bolts and move the engine back a bit as in the *Clutch Mechanism Adjustment* above. If the system works OK, replace any shields you took off, hook up the spark plug wire again, and you're set to mow.

Handle and Grass Catcher

Description

These parts of the power reel mower are exactly the same as those on a hand mower, so see the *Handle* and *Grass Catcher* sections of the *Hand Mower* chapter (page 51).

Chapter 4

Rotary Mower
(Gasoline Powered)

The Rotary mower has a vertical shaft engine with a single bar blade at the lower end of the shaft. It is by far the simplest and cheapest power mower. Unless it is self-propelled, it has no clutch to mess with. It shouldn't really be self-propelled, because the mower is so light and maneuverable that the drive wheels are usually more of a hindrance than a help, except on a big, level, often-mowed lawn, which is better suited for a power reel mower. So the rotary mower, when used in its normal, straightforward form, is a simple, trouble-free machine. *But it's a vicious bugger!* Don't forget that for a split second when you are around one. Rotary mowers probably take off more toes and fingers each year then any contraption made by man.

Shopping Hints

Remember the vicious nature of the whirling rotary blade when you go to buy a mower. Get the lightest one you can. The ones with magnesium housings are the lightest and therefore the easiest to handle. Next lightest are the mowers with aluminum housings. The heavier rotary mowers often have steel housings. But for those of you who still aren't talked out of getting a self-propelled rotary, the heaviest mowers of all in this category are the power-driven ones, even if they have magnesium housings.

The shape of the rotary mower housing is just as important as the weight. The best rotaries have a horn-of-plenty or wind-tunnel shape curving around the front of the housing and ending at the discharge chute, where the grass flies out. There should be a three to five-inch extension of the chute from the housing (see illustration

35). If the mower you are considering has no extension on the chute, look for another, safer mower. A chuteless rotary can fling things out in all kinds of awkward directions, like at your head. Look at the back of the mower. There should be either a hinged deflector flap that rides along touching the ground, or the back of the housing should come down quite low, so rocks can't be thrown out from under the mower at your tootsies (see Appendix, *Appendages,* for more hints on the subject). Most new mowers with these basic safety bases covered have triangular decals on them which say American National Standards Institute. These decals don't absolutely guarantee safety, but they mean that at least some effort has been made.

You should go beyond the bare essentials, though. Consider the placement and size of the wheels, for instance. The more stable, and therefore the safer configuration is the square mower with a wheel at each corner. Don't get a mower with the front right wheel moved back behind the discharge chute. The bigger the wheels, the better, too. Like 7½-inch diameter ones are OK, but 8½-inch ones are much better.

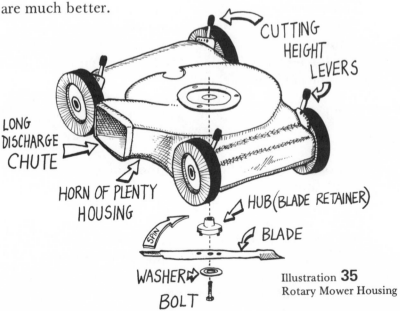

CUTTING HEIGHT LEVERS

LONG DISCHARGE CHUTE

HORN OF PLENTY HOUSING

HUB (BLADE RETAINER)

BLADE

SPIN

WASHER

BOLT

Illustration **35**
Rotary Mower Housing

If the mower you're considering passes the safety tests, check the size of the blade and the power of the engine. For 99 out of 100 people, an 18 to 20-inch blade will be quite sufficient, if matched with a 3 hp (or approximately 8-9 cubic inch) engine. If you are lured by the models with longer blades, remember that they need stronger engines, and that the ends of a longer blade travel that much faster and with that much more destructive force. Keep in mind, too, that the longer the blade, the bigger the housing—the thing will tend to hang up on lumps in the lawn much more than a smaller mower. In other words, the longer blade makes for *more* work, not less, and is dangerous as well.

See if the mower has a convenient setup for raising and lowering the wheels, especially if you will have to raise and lower them often for things like weed mowing or low-cut type grasses (see *Which Mower* on pages 5-9). Most new rotary mowers have little handles sticking up next to each wheel. On other more primitive models, you will have to look under the housing to see the row of holes where each wheel axle goes through the housing. The axles on these models must be unbolted and moved to different holes to adjust the mowing height. Ask if the mower has a Low Compression starter gismo. This is one of the few new-fangled attachments that make sense. It is simple and reliable, and makes the engine so easy to turn over by hand that there is no longer any excuse for a troublesome thing like an electric starter, which will always run out of juice or break down one way or the other.

Look under the housing of the mower if you can without tipping up one side. Often the mowers will be up on racks so you can see under them. If they aren't, get down on your hands and knees, lift one side of the mower just a few inches, and peek under. Look at the way the center of the blade is held to the end of the engine shaft. There will be a bolt through the very middle of the blade for sure, but what you are looking for in particular are two bolts or studs through the blade, one on each side of the main center bolt, or a shaped retainer fixed to the crankshaft, which the blade fits into so that it can't spin loose (see illustrations 35, 38). Check the length of the shaft, too—the shorter the better, because a long shaft will bend more easily.

Wheels

Description

The four round things that the mower rolls on. Boy, are they simple compared to the reel mower wheels. The wheel and its sleeve bearing are simply held to the housing or to a height-adjusting lever by a bolt, nut, and washer (see illustration 36). The washer is often a curved one which keeps the wheel in place while allowing it to shift sideways a bit if the mower receives a blow from one side or the other. A small pinned hubcap sometimes covers the head of the bolt. If the mower has height-adjusting levers, these levers and the wheels are mounted on plates, each of which has several holes or notches in it. Studs on the levers fit into the holes, fixing the wheels in position.

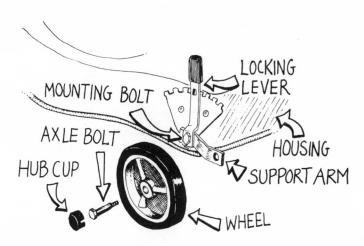

Illustration **36**
Adjustable Wheel

115

Problems

MOWER CUTTING TOO HIGH OR LOW

You're trying to cut the weeds, and the mower keeps running its housing into the ground and snagging on big bunches of week stalks, or piles that dogs have left there over the winter. Or maybe you have to mow your lawn about every four days because the mower is only cutting the grass plants down to about 3 inches tall. One way or the other, you need to do a

CUTTING HEIGHT ADJUSTMENT

Take the mower to a flat place, like a garage floor or a level sidewalk, then check to see if your mower has height-adjusting levers as in illustration 36.

To adjust each lever, all you have to do is move it away from the mower housing (usually until the lever is pushing against the wheel), thus releasing the lever stud from its hole or notch. Push and pull the lever to find out which way moves the wheel up and which way moves it down. What's that? It won't budge? Take an open-end wrench or the crescent wrench and loosen (c-cl) the mounting bolt and its nut inside the housing (see illustration 36). Set the lever in a new notch or hole, the one right next to the position the wheel was in originally. Move the other wheels up or down by one position so the whole mower rests level at its new cutting height, with all four wheels on the ground. Tighten (cl) the mounting bolts and nuts if you loosened them. If you want to move the mower more than you have already, use each wheel lever to set the wheels at the next position in their range. But always change the cutting height by one increment at a time, so you can't get things out of line. If you want to lower the cutting height more than the range of the lever will let you, first put the thing in its lowest position and measure how high the bottom edge of the front of the mower housing is off the level concrete floor or sidewalk. If the mower has only about ¾ inch clearance, don't even consider moving the thing

116

any lower. It'll just scrape and snag on lumps in the lawn surface all the time (if you are meticulous, and have a perfectly level lawn and want to mow it down lower than your mower will, see *Which Mower*—you are using the wrong machine altogether). But let's say you have the cutting height control levers set at their lowest position and the bottom edge of the front of the mower housing is still an inch and a half off the concrete. In that case, check to see if there is more than one hole in the housing for each whole wheel and height-adjusting unit. If there are a row of holes, and the mounting bolt isn't through the top hole in the row, you can lower the cutting height some more. Start by putting the mower up on blocks as in illustration 37, then remove the hubcap, if there is one, by straightening its tabs with a screwdriver from behind the wheel and pulling it off. Loosen (c-cl) the bolt that holds a wheel, and remove the bolt and wheel. Next loosen (c-cl) and remove the mounting bolt that holds the cutting height lever assembly to the mower housing. Keep all the cutting height lever parts on the mounting bolt, and move the bolt to the next higher hole (the higher the assembly is the lower the mower and cutting height will be). Thread (cl) the nut back on the end of the bolt and tighten (cl) it well. Replace the wheel bolt in its hole in the lever assembly and tighten (cl) the nut on. Move the other three wheels and lever assemblies in the same way. When you have all the wheels set in their new positions, check first to see that they all touch the level concrete floor. Then check to make sure that the bottom edge of the front of the mower housing has ¾ inch clearance over the floor. If you have moved the wheels too high in relation to the mower, move them all down a notch or two with the levers. You may well wonder why the mower even has a setting for the lever assemblies that lets you make the cutting height too low. That setting was built into the mower in case you change the wheels to ones that are larger and that therefore require lower cutting height settings (see *Wheel Shot,* below).

On *rotary mowers without height-adjusting levers,*
cutting height adjustment is more tedious. Look behind
a wheel inside the housing for a row of holes. If the holes
are covered with matted grass and dirt, clean the area with
a screwdriver and the wire parts brush. If you can see that
the holes are there, and if you are willing to go to the
trouble of moving all the wheels to change the cutting
height, put the mower up on blocks as in illustration 37.
Undo and ground the spark plug wire (see Frontispiece),
then pry the hubcap off the wheel if it has one, straightening the cap tabs with a screwdriver from behind the
wheel. Feel around inside the housing where a wheel axle
bolt goes through. Is there a nut inside the housing on
the end of the wheel axle bolt? If there is, you have to
get an open-end wrench in there (a crescent wrench will
do, if it'll fit in there, and if you can get it adjusted to fit
the nut) and hold onto the nut while you loosen (c-cl)
the whole axle bolt. More often there won't be a nut; the
housing has threaded holes instead, and the bolt simply
screws into the housing. In this case, just loosen (c-cl) the
bolt and remove it, taking the wheel, bearing and any
washers along with it. Move the whole assembly to a new
hole, the next higher hole if you want to lower the cutting

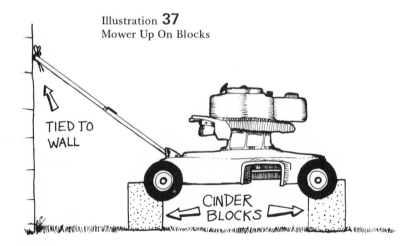

Illustration **37**
Mower Up On Blocks

TIED TO
WALL

CINDER
BLOCKS

height, the next lower hole if you want to raise the cutting height. Repeat the process on all the other wheels, then take the mower down off the blocks and put it on a level concrete surface to check and make sure you have all the wheels in the same position. If one or two wheels are off the ground, or if the whole mower is tipping one way or the other, check the holes to find out which wheel is in the wrong position. When the mower is level, check the distance between the bottom edge of the front of the mower housing and the floor. That distance must be at least ¾ inch. If it isn't, your mower is an oddball, or it has wheels that are too small. You have to account for the mower's oddity by raising the cutting height (lowering the axles) by one or two increments. Wheels all set, and cutting height where you want it? Great. Take the mower down off the blocks, reconnect the spark plug wire, and you're set to mow.

WHEEL SHOT
The rotary blade threw a sprinkler head through one of the tires and cut it right down to the bone. Frightening, the power of that bastard, isn't it? Remember that, and keep your feet out from under it. About the sprinkler head. Some day I'll do a book about plumbing. But for now, let's just take care of the ruined mower wheel.

Find out what the wheel axle bolt is attached to. If there is a hubcap over the head of the axle bolt, remove it by straightening the tabs with a screwdriver from behind the wheel, turning the wheel until each tab appears under the housing. If the axle bolt just goes through the housing, feel around for the end of the bolt in there and determine if there is a nut on it. If the wheel is attached to a lever assembly for height adjusting, there will almost certainly be a nut on the end of the axle bolt. Hold the nut still with an open-end wrench, and loosen (c-cl) the axle bolt, until it and the wheel separate from the rest of the mower. Take the axle out of the wheel and the bearing sleeve. Put the axle bolt on the edge of a flat table so that the head is just hanging over the edge, and the rest of the bolt is sticking in toward the center of the table. Make a test for straightness; roll the bolt along the edge of the table and get your head down so you can sight right along the surface of the table and watch the bolt as it rolls along. Watch for the threaded end of the bolt wobbling up and down as the bolt turns, or for little spaces appearing and disappearing under the smooth bearing surface of the bolt. Either will indicate that the bolt is bent out of shape. If the bolt is bent, take it when you go to get a replacement wheel.

If you have the cutting height adjusting levers on your mower, take a good look at those parts, too, to make sure that the blow that did in your wheel didn't bend the lever assembly, too. You can usually dismantle the assembly by undoing (c-cl) the mounting bolt (see illustration 36), and you might be able to straighten the bent parts by putting them in a vise and carefully working out the bends with a crescent wrench that's adjusted to just slip over the metal. If the part is really scrunched, take it with the wheel and axle bolt for replacement. You may have to wait some time for a replacement for those cutting height assembly parts, though.

Go to a good mower shop to get all the replacements. Hardware stores have wheels and bolts which they claim will work, but they never quite fit right, and often require a lot of shimming and jury rigging before they're functional. When you have your nifty new wheels, look at the two sides and find out which hub side protrudes the farthest. One side will not bulge out as far as the edge of the tire. This will be the outside of the wheel. The other, more protruding side of the wheel, goes against the mower housing, keeping the tire clear of it. Make sure the washer is between the wheel and the housing, too, especially if it's one of those warped washers that alienate (heh) the wheel from the housing by about ¼ inch. If the washer is missing and the wheel has too much play, it'll be hard to control the direction of the mower. Tighten (cl) the bolt thoroughly, and check the wheel to make sure it spins freely. If it's too tight, remove the washer or replace it with a thinner one.

Sometimes it's impossible to find a wheel just the size of the old one. In that case, get two wheels that are near to the same size of the old one, to replace not only the broken wheel but also its partner wheel on the opposite side of the mower. Then measure the radius of the new wheels and relate it to the radius of the old ones. If the new ones have a radius that is, say, ½ inch larger than the old wheels, move the axle position of the new wheels up in relation to the mower housing ½ inch, or as close as you can get to that. See *Cutting Height Adjustment* for hints (page 116).

Blade

Description

Whirling dervish. Instant Amputator. When it's sitting still it is a very innocuous metal bar with sharpened edges, held to the end of the engine crankshaft by a bolt and some kind of shaped hub or retainer as in illustration 38. When the engine is whirling it around and around, you can't even see it, but it is potentially a terrifically destructive weapon. Always respect it as such. And never forget,

before working on the blade, *UNDO AND GROUND THE SPARK PLUG WIRE!*

Problems

BLADE JAMMED
See *Housing Problems;* you need to clean things out.

BLADE NOT CUTTING GRASS
When you run the mower over your lawn, it leaves the grass looking more like the Super Bowl was just played on it. The grass plants get churned and flattened down to the ground, instead of cut off neatly; the mower will cut

better if you run it at the absolute top speed, but even at that it doesn't cut the lawn smoothly.

Disarm the bugger by undoing and grounding the spark plug wire. Put the mower up on blocks like in illustration 37. Get a flashlight and lean down so you can look under the housing at the blade. Is it obviously bent at one end? If it is, you might have noticed the mower shaking around a lot. If the blade is straight, take a close look at the cutting edges. Turn the blade so that it makes a line straight across the mower from one side to the other, then check the cutting edge that's nearest you. On the left side of the mower, the cutting edge is the frontmost one. On the right side of the mower the cutting edge is the rearmost one. Is the cutting edge rounded off, or jagged from where the blade has hit things like rocks and lawn borders? The procedure is the same for a bent, dull, or battered blade. First you are going to take the blade off, then throw it away and buy a new one or sharpen and balance it; then you replace it.

BLADE REMOVAL

Spark plug wire undone and grounded? Good. Take the mower to a smooth flat place like a garage floor or a patio. There are two ways you can position the mower in order to get the blade off. You can either turn it up at a 45 degree angle, which requires the often distasteful task of siphoning the gas out of the gas tank, or you can put the mower up on blocks, which requires a little lifting and a little more agility for the actual blade removal. Take your pick. I abhor the taste of gasoline, so I avoid the tip-up method and put the mower on blocks as in illustration 37.

Here's how to *siphon the gas out* if you want to tip the mower up at a 45 degree angle. Get a 3-foot section of clear plastic fuel line from an auto parts store or a hobby shop (some car shops have little hand siphons for a buck which are dandy if the valves in them work, and which keep the gas away from your mouth). For those of you who get a siphon and aren't familiar with the "Okie Credit

Card," as it is known in the trade, practice with a bucket of nice tasteless water. Put the bucket on a block about 8 inches high, then stick one end of the clear fuel line into the water and hold it there. Suck on the other end of the line until you can see that the column of water is about half way up the tube. Then pinch off the end of the tube that's in your mouth with your fingers, and put that end down on the ground. Release the pinch hold so the water runs down the tube and out onto the ground. Whoopie! Just like in eighth grade science class. Lift up the mouth end of the siphon to make it stop. Practice the process a couple of times. Got the hang of it? Good. Do it on the mower gas tank. You may want to collect the gas in a bowl or bucket, but it's actually better to just run it into the dirt, especially if you can see that there are grass particles in the gas tank. You can use the siphon as a vacuum cleaner, and suck up all that grass-in-the-gas; dirty gas tends to clog up the carburetor. When the gas tank is empty, put the handle at its highest position, push the front of the mower up against a wall, and raise the back of the mower up until the handle is almost to the wall. Pound a nail into the wall at that height and tie the mower handle to it, so the thing can't fall down on you while you're working under it. When the mower is tied up, watch for oil oozing out of the engine, either at the oil fill hole, or around it. If oil is leaking out, you have no choice but to lower the mower to level and put it up on blocks as in illustration 37.

When you have the mower up off the ground one way or the other so you can get at the blade, check out the way the middle of the blade is attached to the end of the shaft that comes down from the engine (see illustration 38). Clear away all dried grass and dirt with a screwdriver and wire brush so you can see what's what. There will be some kind of shaped hub or blade retainer holding the blade in position (the two-stud type is often hard to see because of a big washer under the head of the big screw, which hides the ends of the studs; get a flashlight

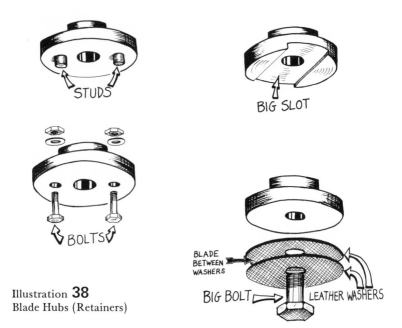

Illustration **38**
Blade Hubs (Retainers)

STUDS

BIG SLOT

BOLTS

BLADE
BETWEEN
WASHERS

BIG BOLT→ LEATHER WASHERS

and look carefully at the hub just above the blade and see if you can catch a glimpse of the stud there). Each kind of hub requires a different blade removal procedure.

On the Big Slot and the Two-Stud models, put a glove on one hand and hold the blade still while you loosen (c-cl) the big hex-head screw that's in the middle of the blade and which goes up into the shaft. Remove the screw and the washer that's under it, and the big round anti-scalp plate, if there is one. Keep all the parts around the screw so you don't lose any. Take the blade off the hub, and go on to the *Sharpening* section below.

On the two-bolt models, put on a glove and grab the blade, then loosen (c-cl) the big hex-head screw that's in the middle of the blade between the two bolt heads. You only have to loosen (c-cl) it a couple of turns. Then get an open-end or box-end wrench on one of the nuts that hold the two bolts. It may be hard to see the nut up in there above the hub. Get a flashlight and shine it across inside the housing as you look through the discharge chute, if the mower is up on blocks. When you have a good grip on the nut with a wrench in one hand, get another wrench on the bolt head with the other hand. Loosen (c-cl) the bolt and remove it, then reach up behind the hub and get the nut and washer that are in there, if they haven't already fallen to the ground. Loosen (c-cl) the other bolt and nut in the same way, but don't remove the bolt. First remove (c-cl) the big center screw, then you can take the last bolt, nut and washer out. Put the bolts, nuts, and washers, along with the big screw and its washer, in a safe place. If there was an anti-scalp plate under all the bolts and nuts, put it on a shelf and leave all the hardware in it like a bowl.

If the blade is held on a simple hub, check to see if there are two holes in the blade, one on each side of the big center screw. If there are two holes, stick a nail through one of them and you can undo the big screw just as in the two-stud process above. If there are no holes, or if the holes are not lined up with the holes in the hub, you must devise a way to hold the shaft still while you loosen the big screw. First just try putting a glove on and holding the blade while you loosen (c-cl) the big screw. Sometimes you can get the screw a bit loose that way, then hold the shaft with one hand under there and unscrew (c-cl) the big screw the rest of the way. Quite often, though, the blade will slip on the end of the shaft and the big screw will stay tight, simply turning the whole shaft around and around. To solve this problem, you have to find a way of holding the shaft in place. The best way is to pin the flywheel. On most Briggs and Stratton, Lawn Boy, Pincor, and Tecumseh engines, there is a space under the flywheel cover where you can stick a screwdriver (see illustration 39). This space will usually be on the opposite side of the engine from the carburetor. Get your head down on the deck of the mower so you can see up into that crack, and turn the blade around by hand so you can watch the flywheel turning around in there. Watch for a shoulder sticking down, or, on mowers with vertical pull starters, watch for gear teeth, either one of which you can jam the screwdriver against and hold it so the engine can't turn the way it normally runs (cl, if viewed from above). Got that? Try several positions of the screwdriver until you get one that holds the flywheel securely. When you put pressure on the wrench to loosen (c-cl from the perspective of under the mower, remember) the big screw, do so slowly, so the flywheel can take the force evenly. If you jerk suddenly on the wrench it might jar the screwdriver loose and damage the flywheel or your hand. Once the big screw is a little loose, you can take the screwdriver out of the flywheel and just reach under the mower and hold onto the shaft with your hand while you finish unscrewing (c-cl) and removing the big screw. Keep the washers and/or the anti-scalp plate on the screw, and take the blade off.

BLADE SHARPENING OR BUYING

Take a good critical look at the blade once you have it off. Are there big gouges in the cutting edges? Are the ends bent differently? The ends are usually bent so that the cutting edge is closer to the ground than the trailing edge, but see if there are other unnatural-looking bends in the blade. If you lay the blade on a flat surface, you can see right away if it's bent. Hammer a nail into a stud of your garage wall so that it sticks out horizontally. Hang the blade on the nail as in illustration 40a. Hit the blade with a hammer. If it rings like a bell, it's sound. If it clunks like the Liberty Bell (very few things in the government ring true anymore), replace the blade. Also, if one end of the blade immediately goes down, mark the heavy end with a marking pen. Turn the blade end for end and hang it on the wall again. Marked end go down again? Make a last check; flip the blade so the other side is toward you, and hang it up on the nail again. The marked end go right to the bottom again? That means the blade is out of balance. If the thing is either badly bunged up, bent, or way

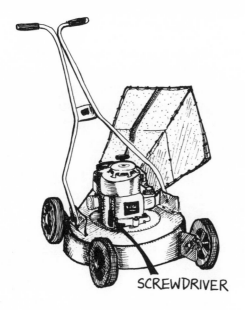

Illustration **39**
Pinning Flywheel

SCREWDRIVER

out of balance, take it to a good mower shop (not a
cheapo discount store) and get an exact replacement, not
only the same size and with the same mounting arrangement, but also, if possible, the same brand as the old one.
When you have your nice new blade, skip to the *Blade
Replacement* procedure, below. But if the blade is close
to balanced and only dull, not battered, then you can
sharpen and balance it and it'll work like new.

Hold the blade in a vise or with a C-clamp while you
sharpen it, and put the jaws of the vise or clamp near one
end of the blade at a time, so the thing can't bend and
quiver around. You can grind the blade with a big grinding
wheel, but this will dig into it so fast that it'll tend to
unbalance it. Better is a small, fine-grain wheel, that'll
fit in an electric drill. If you can find a Black and Decker
lawnmower sharpening attachment for your drill, that's
great. Remember to wear safety goggles, whichever wheel
you use. The most reliable way is to just use a fine-grade
metal file and hand-sharpen the blade. Whichever way
you choose to do the sharpening, do it at the same angle
as the original cutting surface on the blade.

If you're doing the job by hand, remember that hand filing is a one-directional process. Push the file against the blade only when you are moving the file away from you. This is the way the file is intended to cut. If you drag the file back across the blade on the return stroke, it'll dull the file, and it won't sharpen the blade much either. Also, it is best to use a diagonal stroke that moves along the cutting edge as well as across it. If you file in one place only, it will make the cutting edge uneven. File only as much as needed to make the round edge sharp again; you don't have to sharpen more than the outer 2 inches of the blade edge—when the blade is whirling around at its frightful speed, only the end of it is doing the cutting. Try to file equal amounts off each end of the blade. If you have to do a little extra filing on one end to get rid of a gouged-out place, remember to take some extra off the other end, too.

When the cutting edges are nice and shiny and sharp (careful with the pinkies—the blade doesn't have to be whirling to cut one off), dull them very *slightly* with the file. About two strokes of the file on the very edge will take off the thin, fragile corner so it's strong, but still close to sharp so it will cut well. Do an accurate balancing

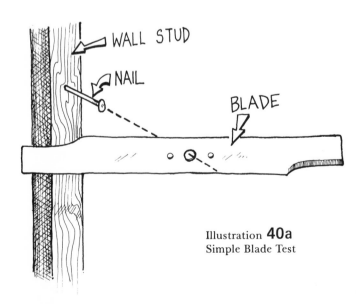

WALL STUD

NAIL

BLADE

Illustration **40a**
Simple Blade Test

test to make sure you haven't filed too much off one end or the other. Put a knife in a vise with the sharp edge up, as in illustration 40b. Put a white piece of paper under the knife, and balance the blade as shown. The blade of the knife should divide the center hole of the mower blade exactly in half when the mower blade is balanced. If irregularities in the surface of the mower blade make it hard to balance, turn the blade over and balance it on the other side. File extra weight off the heavy side until you get the blade perfectly balanced or very close to it.

BLADE REPLACEMENT

No matter which kind of hub setup you have, the first step of putting your new or sharp, balanced blade back on is arranging the washers and/or the anti-scalp plate in order on the big center screw. Put the big screw up through the blade so that the sharp edges of the blade are forward if the blade is spun clockwise, the way the engine runs (some very rare birds run counterclockwise; if the engine turns that way when you pull the rope, put the blade on so it cuts going counterclockwise). Hold the threaded end of the screw and let the blade hang resting on the screw head and washer; the sharp edges of the blade should be the leading ones if you spin the blade clockwise. Look at illustration 35. Is your blade positioned like that one? Good. Turn the screw (cl) most of the way into the shaft, and get the blade aligned on the studs, in the big slot, or under the two bolt holes in the hub. If you have the two-

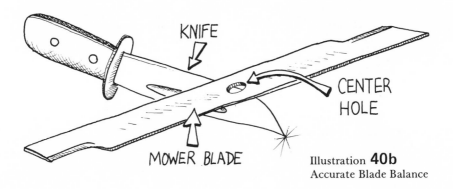

KNIFE

CENTER HOLE

MOWER BLADE

Illustration **40b**
Accurate Blade Balance

129

bolt kind of hub, replace the bolts, the washers, and the nuts, and snug them up (cl). If you have the simple type of hub that has two holes, why not convert it to a two-bolt type with two little bolts, nuts, and washers? Snug up (cl) the bolts and nuts. Tighten (cl) the big center screw thoroughly on all two-bolt blades before you tighten (cl) the bolts and nuts. On any kind of setup, make sure the big screw is very thoroughly tight, even if this means pinning the flywheel again with a screwdriver as in illustration 39, or holding the blade with a gloved hand. An extra precaution can be taken to prevent cutting yourself on that new or freshly sharpened blade. Hold the blade just toward the center from the sharpened part of the edge. This will give you plenty of leverage to tighten (cl) the big screw, and limit the odds of that blade slipping and going right through the glove into your hand.

Take the mower down off its blocks, or tip it back down on its wheels, then refill the gas tank with fresh gas if you siphoned all the gas out. Hook up the spark plug and start the engine. Does the mower shake more than it used to? If so, you haven't balanced the blade properly. If the mower shook before the blade worked, and still shakes even though you balanced the blade meticulously, then the cause of the shakiness of the mower is not the blade but the crankshaft. Go to *Bad Vibrations* (page 166) *Engine* chapter. If the mower is working smoothly, go try it out on the lawn. It's wonderful how much difference a sharp blade makes. You can run the engine at about half the speed, and it'll still just go through the grass like shit through a goose. Which brings something to mind. Clean the dog piles off the lawn before you try out your nice sharp mower.

BLADE LOOSE
The mower shakes and makes a horrible racket when it runs, or you can't get it started and were sent here from the engine trouble shooting guide.

Stop the mower engine, undo and ground the spark

plug wire, and get the bottom of the mower up where you can see it as in the beginning of the *Blade Removal* procedure. When the mower is up, check to see that the bolts in the middle of the blade, the ones that hold it to the shaped hub or retainer, are all thoroughly tightened (cl).

As you tighten the bolts, you may notice that the hub or retainer slips around the engine shaft. If this is the case, loosen (c-cl) the bolts or screw and bolts that hold the blade in place. To keep the shaft still while you loosen the big center screw, you may have to pin the flywheel by sticking a screwdriver against a shoulder of it as in illustration 39. When you have the blade and all its fastening hardware off, try to slide the loose hub off the shaft. It may take some twisting and pulling. If the thing will twist around the shaft, but won't come off, you have to take it to a mower shop and have them pull it off, or buy a pulley puller from a car shop and do the job yourself (see *Tools* in Appendix). If you can get the hub off, get the remains of the little half-circle key (the woodruff key) out of the slots in the shaft and the hub. Get a new key that fits the slots from a mower shop or machine shop— there are only a few standard sizes for mowers, so it won't be hard to get an exact replacement. Put the key into the slot in the shaft and slip the hub into place with its groove aligned to the key. Tap the hub firmly into place.

Replace the blade, making sure all the bolts and nuts and the big center screw are thoroughly tightened (cl). If the mower is still difficult to start, go back to the engine trouble shooting guide. If the mower still shakes, take the blade off and see *Blade Sharpening*, above.

Housing

Description

The molded or stamped metal cover that is over the blade of the mower. It is most often made of steel, but on more sophisticated mowers it can be made of aluminum or even cast magnesium for lightness.

Problems

HOUSING OR DISCHARGE CHUTE CLOGGED,
OR BLADE JAMMED

You mowed the lawn when it was still wet, and the wet, sticky clippings and bits of mud made a beautiful plaster all over the underside of the housing and maybe even over the discharge chute.

DANGER   DANGER   DANGER   DANGER   DANGER

Don't, for god's sake, reach into the chute to clear out the clippings while the mower is running. Don't kick at the chute to knock the matted clippings off either. You'll miss having your toes almost as much as your fingers.

Turn off the mower's engine. Undo and ground the spark plug wire, too (see Frontispiece). A mower that has been running can start up again terribly easily. Like if you just turn the blade once under there, to get it out of your way as you clean the housing.

Before you start the actual cleaning, figure out how to prop the mower up to get under there. Check the gas tank to see how much gas there is in it. If there is less than half a tank, you can simply close the fuel shut-off valve if there is one under the gas tank, and tip the back of the mower up to about a 45 degree angle. This is easiest to do if you push the front of the mower up against a wall, then lift the handle up and tie it to a nail pounded into the wall about five feet up. Don't tip the mower up sideways; if you do, and the gas tank winds up over the cylinder, gas can leak down through the carburetor and into the cylinder and even into the oil, which will make the engine impossible to start. If you make that mistake, see quickie test 1 in the *Engine* chapter, page 158. If you have more than a half tank of gas, and are worried about getting gas all through the engine, siphon out some of the gas as in the first part of the *Blade Removal* procedure on page 122.

If the grass and mud plaster stuck to the housing is still wet, you can scrape it off with a stick or your fingers. But if it's dry, you have to pry off chunks with a screwdriver, and clean the rest with the wire parts brush. The more thorough you are about cleaning the old stuff off, the longer it will stay off, especially if the housing has that horn-of-plenty or wind tunnel shape.

On a few elaborate models of rotary mower there is a hole in the housing where you can stick a hose and supposedly just shoot a little water in (without a nozzle on the hose) while the mower is still running, and clean off all the clippings and mud. It's a nice idea, and it even works if the grass is dry and there isn't any mud mixed in with it. But if you try the spray-clean method and find that the mower sprays water all over the place but leaves a lot of grass-plaster under the housing, disarm the mower by undoing and grounding its spark plug wire, and do the cleanout procedure as described in the preceding paragraphs.

Handle

Description

The thing you push when you're using the mower. It is usually made of tubular steel, and most often has a lower half and an upper half, which are bolted together. The lower half of the handle is attached to the rest of the mower by studs or sometimes by a bolt and nut arrangement.

Problems

HANDLE FALLS OFF

You mowed down to the end of your lawn and then made one of those sweeping turn-around motions like you've seen the pro gardeners do, and the handle swung around, but the mower went right on into the petunias.

First turn the mower off and undo the spark plug wire. Then determine whether a bolt-and-nut arrangement was supposed to be holding the handle on, or a stud with some kind of pin on it.

If a bolt-and-nut set came undone, you've probably lost some of the parts. Undo (c-cl) the ones on the other side that didn't come off, and go get replacements at a hardware store. Chances are the handle bent when one side of it came unhooked, so use your vise grips and a little discretion to straighten the flat end of the handle back out again. Don't grab the tubular part of the handle with the vise grips; just put them on the already flattened end section, and grab the rest of the handle with your bare hands to do the bending. It may take a friend and some puffing and sweating, but get the thing back to the right shape so it will slip into place ready for that new bolt-and-nut set. If you couldn't get exactly the same type of bolt and nut that came on the mower, you can make do with a bolt and two nuts locked together in many cases. The idea is to put the bolt in and snug the first nut up (cl) on the handle and bracket, then back it off about ¼ turn (c-cl) and tighten (cl) the second nut up against the first. This will hold the handle in position without bolting it so tight that the handle can't move up and down.

On handles that are simply stuck over a stud (a short pole), look first for a little hole through the stud right near its end. There should be a cotter pin or at least a bent nail through that little hole. If the hole is pinless, that will be part of the reason that the handle came off. The other part of the reason is probably that the handle, instead of pressing its ends onto the studs, was loose and flobby so that it slipped off easily. First fix that handle flobbiness, then take care of the missing or shot cotter. On most mowers, the handle ends press out against the studs. To make them stay put, spread the ends apart until they naturally stay about 3 to 4 inches wider apart than the studs. Then pull them together just enough to get the ends over the studs, and let them snap on firm. On some mowers the handles press in on the studs. Obviously, on these models, you squeeze the ends of the handle closer together so they will hold in place on the studs. When the handle

ends are holding themselves firmly in place, get a couple
of cotter pins that'll fit through the little holes (3/32 x 1
inch is the most common size). Push a pin through its hole,
start spreading the ends apart with a screwdriver, then
wrap the ends in opposite directions around the stud with
a pair of pliers. Now you can go back and try that fancy
swooping turn down at the end of the lawn with no fear
of ruining any more petunias. Do watch your feet as you
swing the mower around, though. You can always plant
a new bed of petunias, but toes never grow back the same
after transplanting.

HANDLE TOO HIGH OR TOO LOW
Either you practically have to do a chin-up to reach the
handle and push the mower, or the handle is so low you
can't get the mower's front wheels off the ground without
touching your toes.
　　There are two basic means of raising and lowering
the height of the handle. On some mowers with two-piece
handles, the upper half of the handle has a bend in it.
This bend can be changed, by flipping the top half of the
handle (see next paragraph) to either raise or lower the
height of the part of the handle you push. On other
mowers the whole handle can be held in different positions by the means of attachment to the rest of the mower.
Check on your mower for the reversible bent upper part
of the handle, or the adjustable stud or mounting bolt
down at the mower itself. Don't be surprised if your
mower has neither adjusting system.
　　If you have the bent upper half of the handle, change
the handle height by first unbolting (c-cl) the control lever,
if there is one, then unbolting (c-cl) both sides of the
upper half of the handle and turning it over so that the
bend goes the opposite way from how it was originally.
Put all the bolts back in place and tighten (cl) them thoroughly, including the ones that hold the control lever in
place.
　　On mowers that have some kind of movable means

of attachment that holds the handle to the mower housing, look closely at that attachment. Often there will be several holes for the bolt or stud that holds the end of the handle in place, or there will be a second bolt or stud against which the handle rests, limiting how low it can swing. Move the handle and see what it hits to prevent it from going lower than it does. Then either undo (c-cl) the attaching bolt, or straighten and remove the pin in the end of the movable stud, and change its position. When the bolt is tight (cl) or the pin replaced, repeat the procedure on the other handle end, so that the handle won't wind up cockeyed. On some mowers, like the Jacobsen, there is a safety bracket that has to be moved along with the movable stud. When both ends of the handle are fixed in their new positions, try pushing the mower without starting it up to make sure you moved the handle the way you meant to.

Self-Propelling Unit

Description

I thought I told you not to buy a self-propelled rotary mower. But you already have one, or maybe you got talked into buying one. You got sold on one, in other words. I know this is completely out of context, but have you ever thought how backwards the notion of being sold on something is? I mean, are you the buyer or are you a product, made to be sold like a car with planned, advertising-induced obsolescence built into it?

But to describe the mower, the self-propelled unit is driven by a chain or belt from the drive shaft of the engine. A gear box usually turns a horizontal axle, and the wheels are turned by this axle. Some models have a big chain or belt driven movable unit which rises up off and settles down onto the wheels.

Problem

DRIVE UNIT SLIPPING OR GNASHING

The self-propellor ain't propelling the mower. Now, if it were my mower, I'd thank my lucky stars that the contraption couldn't get in my way anymore, and I'd use the thing the way I would any normal rotary mower. But if you want to try to get the self-propelling unit working again, there might be some simple adjustments you can make.

If there is a lever and rod control system for the thing, look on the mower end of the rod and see if there is a threaded section that you can twist, or a sleeve or nut that you can twist, clockwise to make the thing disengage sooner, counterclockwise to make it engage sooner.

If there is a cable and housing type control system, look for a clamp screw holding the housing near the mower end (like the clamp screws in illustrations 29b and d). Loosen (c-cl) the screw and adjust the position of the housing to either tighten or loosen the clutch. Tighten (cl) the clamp screw and try the thing out before you start the motor, to make sure you have it right.

Look at the gear box that turns the horizontal bar if there is one on your model. There is often an adjusting screw with a locknut around it at the edge of this gear box. If the tip of this screw is touching, or almost touching the mower housing, then it can be used to tighten up the gear box. Loosen (c-cl) the locknut and tighten (cl) the adjusting screw until it is just snug against the mower housing. No tighter. Tighten (cl) the locknut to fix the screw in that snug position, and the gears should work.

If you have an adjusting screw next to the gear box that doesn't snug against the mower housing, but rather tightens and loosens the belt, you can adjust your setup too. Turn the screw (cl usually, but not always) so that the belt is just a bit tighter than it was when the unit was slipping. On most but not all units, you should be able to squeeze the belt, between the pulleys, until there is one inch between the sides of it. This will mean that the belt is tight, but not straining when the mower is in gear. Try the drive unit out without starting the engine. If you can see that the belt is tight as a drum now, use the adjusting screw to loosen things up.

If these adjustments don't help your sick self-propelling mower, take it to the shop where you bought it and face the music; costly repairs and looong waits for parts. I warned you.

Chapter 5
Electric Rotary Mower

Description and Shopping Hints

Most electric rotary mowers on the market are very similar. They consist of a rotary blade much like that of a gas-powered rotary mower, and a simple electric motor, the armature of which drives the blade. If you want to spend a little extra money when buying one, try to get a mower with a more powerful motor (like 1 or 1½ hp instead of ¾ hp), or one with safety features like a deflector plate that travels along behind the mower.

All of the parts of the electric mower are the same as those of the gas-powered rotary, with the exception of the motor and the few things listed below. Therefore, if you have a problem, and it isn't covered below, it will be covered in the procedures for the gas-powered rotary. Keep in mind, however, that for each time the procedure tells you to "undo and ground the spark plug wire," you can simply substitute, "undo the extension cord."

Blade

Description

The electric rotary mower blade is pretty much like its gas-powered cousin. But on many models, there are extra things mounted on the same bolt or shaft (called the armature, instead of the crankshaft) that holds the blade (see illustration 41). There is often a fan mounted above the blade, and insulating washers on either side of the blade. Lastly, there is a flat-sided segment of the shaft that matches a retainer washer, and the blade is held in place by a nut instead of a big hex screw.

Problems

MOWER WON'T CUT GRASS

The motor is working and the blade is whirling around,
but it just mashes and mangles the grass instead of cutting
it evenly.

   The blade removal and sharpening procedures are
all the same as those for the gas-powered mower, but you
don't have any spark plug wire to ground, so you unplug
the extension cord. You don't have any gas and oil to
worry about (isn't that nice!), so you can just tip the
mower up on its side to work on the blade. Look carefully at the things that are holding the blade to the armature shaft. Clean off any grass and mud to get a clear view.

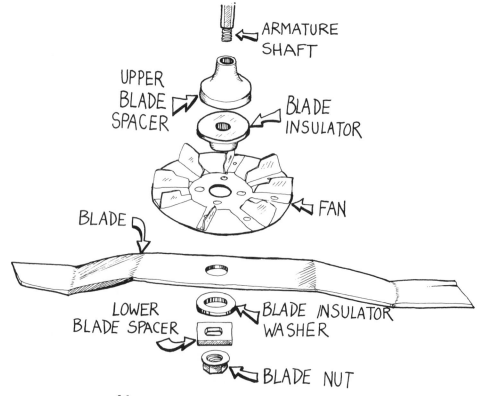

Illustration **41**
Electric Rotary Blade

If you have a setup like the gas-powered blade, with two little bolts and a big screw, or two studs holding the blade in place, remove the blade as if it were a gas-powered one. To remove a Black and Decker blade, like in illustration 41, or any similar one, just hold the blade with a gloved hand, and loosen (c-cl) the big nut on the end of the armature shaft.

Sharpen the blade just as if it were a gas-powered one. Pay special attention to keeping the blade balanced, and if you can't get the thing satisfactorily balanced because of dings or over-sharpening on one side, don't hesitate to get a new blade. An unbalanced blade will ruin an electric mower much faster than it'll do a gas mower in. And a new blade only costs about three bucks.

When you start to reconstruct the blade setup with your nice shiny new or sharpened blade, make sure you have the parts in the right order so that the blade will be insulated in case of a short in the motor. Also, on the Black and Decker type, make sure the lower blade spacer is fitted onto the flat sides of the armature shaft. Tighten whichever setup you have thoroughly. That mower may be quieter than the gas-powered ones, but it can wreak just as much havoc if its blade comes off.

Extension Cord

Description

The long wire that connects the mower to the plug in the wall. It can have two leads (or wires) like an ordinary house appliance, or it might have three leads and three prongs like a big power tool or washing machine. It must be 16 gauge wire if it is 50 to 100 feet long, 14 gauge up to 200 feet long, and 12 gauge for anything longer than 200 feet.

PROBLEMS

ZAP! The mower gives you a shock. If the cord is one of the two-prong type, switch the prongs in the outlet. This may remove the short that caused the shock. If the cord is one of the three-prong kind, and you cheated and put it into a two-prong socket, get an adapter with a ground wire on it so that you can ground away shocking experiences like you just had. Check the cord, especially where it is attached to the off-on switch, for fraying. If it is shot, get a replacement cord from a shop. Don't try repairing the old one, it isn't worth the chance. Check the off-on switch for looseness or broken connections, and check the wire that goes from the switch to the motor. If there is any reason to suspect these parts, take the mower to a good shop and have them do the electrician's work—don't start monkeying around with a soldering iron unless you are enough of an electrician to know which parts will and which parts will not be damaged by heating.

CORD BROKEN

You ran over the cord with the mower, right? Makes a wild scene, doesn't it? That terrific racket, and the cord flailing all over for a brief second, and then that complete silence of a dead machine. Unplug the extension cord immediately when it happens.

While you're sitting on the lawn trying to untangle the goddam thing, don't be surprised if your snide neighbor comes over and says "Hey, whatcha doing? Something wrong with the electric mower?" As if he didn't know. Him and his gas mower. If you want to know how to fix him good, just pour a bottle of coke into the gas tank of his smoggy, noisy old mower when he isn't looking. That'll fix him. Ecotage, I think they call it. Sabotage in ecological disguise.

But a much better idea than petty revenge is learning how to avoid getting your nice quiet electric mower tangled up in its extension cord. When you have taken the ruined cord off the blade and replaced it with a nice new one (don't try to patch the old cord, it'll never be safe and waterproof; also, get a cord that's heavy enough, at least 16 gauge for cords up to 100 feet long, 14 gauge up to 200 feet), set a little time aside to learn the "Manolete Mower Turn," which was perfected by the immortal bullfighter of that name.

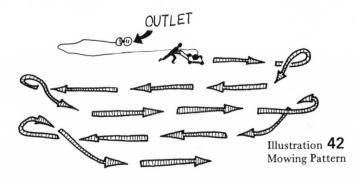

Illustration **42**
Mowing Pattern

Practice on some early, foggy Saturday morning so your neighbor won't have a reason for more unwanted remarks. Don't plug the extension cord in for the practice session, just tie its end to a chair leg or something so it'll stay put as if it were plugged in. Then pretend you're mowing the lawn. Start at the side of the lawn that's nearest where you tied the plug down. Go from one end of that side to the other (see illustration 42). Now get ready for the turn; keep the hand that's closest to the plug (or the chair you tied the end of the cord to) firmly on the mower handle. Grab the cord with the other hand, about a foot away from the place where it's fixed to the mower handle. Turn the mower *toward* the tied-down end of the cord (this is the opposite of what you'd expect) and at the same time give the cord a graceful flip right over the front of the mower. Practice this flip and loop turn method until you can do it with a flourish, and *without* running over the cord. Got it down to an art? ¡Olé!

Now you can show the neighborhood skeptic a thing or two. And when the world really runs low on gas, and still has electricity from reactors of one sort or another, you can show him another thing or two.

Motor

Description

The electric motor on your rotary mower is a wonderfully simple and care-free mechanism. Don't tamper with it unless you have to. It consists of carefully balanced and aligned parts that must be kept in their proper positions and both clean and dry. They are therefore covered with a tight, solid cover, that you should not remove unless it's absolutely necessary.

Problems

MOTOR WON'T START

Unplug the extension cord from the wall socket, and try plugging something else into the socket, like a lamp, just to see if you have any juice at all. Then try using a different extension cord. If the original extension cord is the troublemaker, don't try to repair it unless the problem is in the plug head, and the head is the kind you can take apart and rewire without special tools. Replace any extension cord that is in the least way questionable. For a couple of bucks, you'll save yourself from some very hair-raising experiences, so why not blow the couple of bucks?

If you find that the problem is with neither the outlet nor the extension cord, take a critical look at the on-off switch. Is it loose and flobby, or cracked, or is the wire going into it cracked and frayed? It should be replaced, by a qualified electrician, if it has any of these problems. Don't do the job yourself with your handy soldering gun; you might melt some essential part of the motor together.

If you eliminate all possibilities except the motor, take the mower to a good shop that does service on your kind of machine, and have them do the brush and armature overhaul, or, if necessary, replace the motor.

MOTOR STOPS

Turn it off and unplug it. NOW. Don't start poking around the motor or underneath the housing until you have unplugged the bugger as well as turned it off. This is for the mower's sake as well as yours. If the motor is stuck and left on, it can cook itself. It just tries and tries to work until it heats up to the melting point. And once the motor is melted together, all the king's horses and all the king's how-to books can't help you unmelt it. OK?

When you have unplugged the mower, check first to make sure nothing has gotten stuck between the blade and the housing. Then make sure the blade can spin around. On some models there is a reverse magnet setup that makes it hard to push the blade around when the mower is shut off, but even on these models you should be able to turn the blade around smoothly on its bearings. If turning the blade makes all kinds of grinding and knuckling noises, the bearings are shot. If the blade is frozen in place, and there's no grass or gunk holding it still, the bearings or the motor must be shot. In any case, the mower needs the care of an expert. Take it to a shop that deals with your kind of mower, and hope it's the bearings and not the whole motor.

Illustration **43**
Oiling Electric Motor

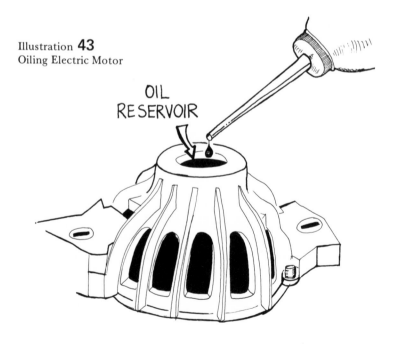

OIL
RESERVOIR

MOTOR SQUEAKY

When you turn the mower on, it squeaks right as it starts up. It makes a very high-pitched whine when it is running, and screeches to a halt when you turn it off. The motor needs oil. If there is an oil hole in the cover over the motor, give it two good squirts. Otherwise, unscrew (c-cl) the screws holding the cover. On some models there is only one screw and a couple of tabs holding the cover in place. On these models, be careful not to break the tabs as you slowly wiggle and work the cover free and off. On all models, remove the cover with extreme caution, making sure that you don't yank the cord and pull it off the poles that it's soldered to on the motor. If you do break the leads off the poles, have a pro do the resoldering; it can be a tricky process.

When you have the cover off, look for an oil reservoir right at the top of the motor. It'll be a round hole with either a piece of felt in it, or a piece of felt covered with a little round piece of plastic (see illustration 43). Take an oil can and put about three to five drops of 20 weight oil in the reservoir. *No more!* That's all it takes. Mush the oil around in the felt, and replace the little cover if there was one. Ease the whole motor cover back into place, making sure that the tabs or screws are setting in the right holes, and tighten (cl) the screws well. *Don't* start the motor without replacing the cover. On many mowers, the cover is a part of the insulating system, and without it the motor can short out and zap you.

If the mower continues to squeak, the bearings or the motor itself might be going out, so you should take the thing to a shop to be serviced. The bearings are usually sealed and self-lubricating, but they do dry out eventually and require replacement.

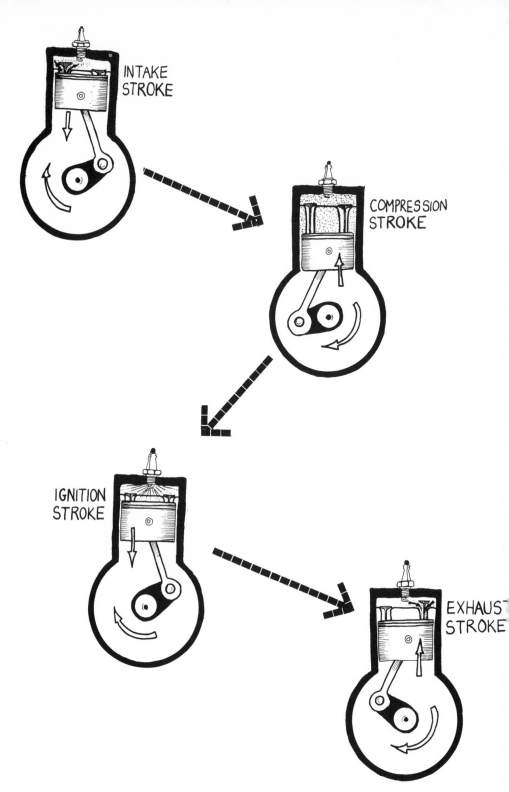

INTAKE
STROKE

COMPRESSION
STROKE

IGNITION
STROKE

EXHAUST
STROKE

Illustration **44**
The Four Strokes
Plus The Final Stroke

Chapter 6
Gas Engine

"The Internal Combustion Engine is
hell-bent on self-destruction"

—David S. Skillman, Ex-mechanic

No further description is needed at this point. If you can
understand the quote and diagram after looking at each
for about five minutes, you know enough. I'm not going
to bore you with stuff like displacement, stroke, bore,
torque ratings, and brake horsepower. Who cares? What
you want to know is how to buy a good mower engine,
how to *start* one, and how to keep it running. OK? Do
familiarize yourself with your engine's name and model
number, though. I mean, how can you tell if I'm talking
about your engine if you don't know its name? Get the
name and mumber off the nameplate, the little square
black piece of tin that's riveted to the engine. The two
most common brand names are Briggs and Stratton (my
favorite, by far) and Tecumseh. Tecumseh engines, with
some minor changes, are on Craftsman, Toro, Reo, and
Lausen machines, so if you have an engine that says one
of those names and doesn't say Tecumseh right
on it, you can treat it like a Tecumseh anyway.
Any machine with a Briggs and Stratton
engine will say B & S right on the engine.

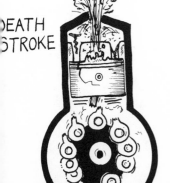

DEATH
STROKE

Shopping Hints

When you are looking at mowers,
pay as much or more attention to
the engine as anything else. Get an

149

engine that's powerful enough to do the job, like a 2½ hp (approximately 7 cubic inch) one for an 18 inch rotary blade or reel length, and at least a 3 hp (approximately 9 cubic inch) for a 20 inch blade or longer. But you want the simplest engine that will fill your needs. Briggs and Stratton and Tecumseh make good, simple, reliable machines. The basic Briggs and Stratton engine is, in fact, an elegant masterpiece of engineered simplicity. But look for the simplest model engine, no matter which brand you might buy. Like for instance, the model with the starter you wrap up yourself, or the one that has a rope that rewinds itself and you have to pull it to start the engine. *Not* the one with the electric starter or the crank-and-release starter. These are complicated and have more parts to get messed up.

Don't get a mower with a two-cycle engine, either. They are quite simple, it's true, but they make an awful racket, a stinking cloud of blue smoke, and a big pain in the neck because you have to put the exact right amount of oil in each time you add gas, or they won't start. So stick to the four-cycle engines, like Briggs and Stratton and Tecumseh. They're simpler to use even if they *do* have more moving parts.

Check the carburetor on any engine you're looking at. If you're not too sure which part of the engine is the carburetor, find the gas tank; the carburetor will be the complicated thing either sitting on top of the gas tank, or, if the gas tank is up high on the engine, the complicated thing attached to the tank by the fuel line, a small, clear or black rubber tube. When you have found the carburetor, take a good look at it. Is there a bowl sticking down from the carburetor? This is the distinguishing mark of a bowl-type carb (see illustration 66a), and all bowl-type carbs require some finicky adjustments. If there is no bowl, the carburetor might be a diaphragm type (see illustration 66b). These are a bit simpler, in most cases. On the simplest engines, though, the gas tank will be directly under the carburetor. This kind of carburetor sucks the gas right into the engine. It is therefore called a suction carburetor, and is very simple indeed, if you keep the gas tank at least ¼ full of fresh clean gas. There are a few basic variations on the suction carburetor, and a great, great number of complicated variations on the bowl and diaphragm types.

If you are looking at a mower with a bowl or diaphragm type carburetor, see how many adjustment screws there are on it. These are the screws whose heads stick out from the body or bowl of the carb, and which have springs around them so you can set them at any one position and have some hope that they will stay there. On some bowl type carbs, there is an adjusting screw that looks more like a miniature water spigot, sticking down from the bottom of the bowl. But whatever the adjusting screws look like, the less there are, the less adjusting you will have to do, and the less the carb will get out of adjustment and fouled up. On old carbs, there was a need for all those adjustable thingies to help the carb adapt to different conditions, like warm and cold weather, or low and high altitude, or good and bad gas. But the later-vintage carbs are so designed that they will give you reasonably good performance under all but the most extreme conditions. So get the carburetor with the least adjustable screws, and if possible, get one with suction feed instead of a bowl.

Whichever engine you get, make sure you get the owner's manual with it. This manual will tell you things about your engine that I can't. Little specifications of adjustments on the engine that only the manufacturer can know for each model. It will also give you a number of hints that I may repeat, but that are well worth seeing twice. So get the manual and read it, as well as the Appendix sections about appendages and tools, and the Prestart section just below *before* you try to fire the engine up. If you lose the owner's manual, write to the parts distributor nearest you, give them the model number of your engine and a stamped, self-addressed envelope, and they'll send you a new manual for free.

Pre-Start Preparations

Don't start your engines, gentlemen (and ladies). Make sure the engine has these three things before you pull the starter: an adequate stop mechanism, a crankcase full (but not too full) of the right oil, and a tank full of fresh clean gasoline.

First check the stop mechanism. There's nothing worse than a mower you can start and get into trouble with, but not stop. Look at the spark plug. If it has a piece of metal that sticks up over it, the "stop spring" as in illustration 45, you're in luck. All you have to do is push that spring against the tip of the plug and the mower will sputter to a halt. Very satisfying. On many modern mowers, though, the stop switch is on the carburetor. Look in your owner's manual for the location of the stop switch on your mower. If you lost the manual or never had one, just look at the part of the carburetor that moves when you move the control lever or knob back and forth. There will be a plate that pivots around a bolt or rivet, and this plate will have a little arm that sticks out and makes contact with a thin brass or copper-colored metal blade when the control is in the stop position. Or at least, that's how it *should* work. Move the control lever in and out of the stop position several times, and look for that tiny little brass blade back in the works. It's often hard to see amidst all the other levers, connecting wires, and springs, but you can find it if you get your head down there and look hard. On new mowers it will in fact stop the mower. But on any mower that's been used heavily or abused, the thin blade will very likely be broken or worn down or disconnected so that it no longer makes contact with the little arm of the plate that swings around over it. So you turn the control lever to "Stop" and the goddam engine goes right on putting as if you had done nothing. On any mower which has a defunct stopping system, add a home-made stop spring, made out of sturdy galvanized sheet metal, or "flashing," as it is often called.

HOME MADE
¾"×3"
METAL STRAP

BEND HERE

⅜" HOLE

Illustration **45**
Stop Spring

Get a piece from a hardware store or a heating and air conditioning contractor, and cut and bend it like the one in illustration 45. Make sure the blower housing bolt that you put the spring under is thoroughly tight (cl to 15 foot pounds on Tecumseh engines, 6 foot pounds on Briggs and Stratton engines).

As for oil, if you only use the mower when the temperatures are well above freezing (why do a nasty job like mowing the lawn when it's cold outside, anyway?), get 30 weight oil, known specifically as "SAE 30 Detergent Oil, For Service SC (or SD or MS)" in the trade. You don't need to know what all those terms mean. I forget myself. Just go to a car parts store or a service station, and get exactly that oil. If you want to start out your relationship with your engine on good terms, give it Pennzoil for its first breakfast. It'll love you for the treat.

If you must mow the lawn at low temperatures, like below freezing (man, you are *weird*), then get "SAE 5W-30 Detergent Oil, for Service SC or SD or MS." Do *not* use any oil marked "For Service MM or ML," and don't put any additives in the oil.

Put the mower on a level surface when you're ready to put oil in it. Find the oil fill plug. It will be either sticking up prominently above the engine, or set right down at the base of the engine, as in illustration 46. While you're looking at illustration 46, introduce yourself to the other named parts of the engine so you will be familiar with them later on. Then unscrew or pull out the oil plug with your bare hands, if you can. If you can't get the plug off easily, use a crescent wrench on the tab of two poles sticking up off it. Get a clean funnel that has a narrow (3/8 inch or less) hole at the bottom. Make two holes in the oil can just as if it were a beer can. Set the funnel in place so that the bottom of it is barely sticking into the oil fill hole (see illustration 46). This way, you will be able to watch the oil pour into the crankcase. Pour the oil through the funnel slowly, so it doesn't overflow either the crankcase or the funnel.

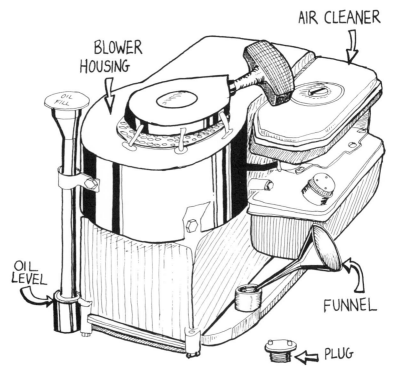

Illustration **46**
Oil Fills

How full do you fill the crankcase? A very important question. Neither over-fill it, nor leave it only partly full. On engines with the oil fill hole down at the base, the idea is to fill the crankcase until oil almost overflows. This can be tricky. If the oil fills up to the top of the hole, stop pouring and wait a minute to make sure the hole hasn't just gotten stopped up a little. If the hole is stopped up by a bubble, the oil will slowly sink into the crankcase, so you can pour in some more. But if the oil level stays at a point about ¼ inch below the top of the oil fill hole, you know you've filled the crankcase. *Don't* ever tip the engine up so you can get more oil into the case. This extra oil will either blast out the seals of the engine, or come spraying out the breather and foul up the air cleaner and possibly the carburetor.

On engines with the extended oil fill hole that sticks up above the blower housing prominently, you must be especially careful not to over-fill. All of these engines hold a little over a pint of oil. That means about half a quart oil can. If you want to be on the safe side, measure out a pint and pour it into the fill hole through your trusty funnel. Wait a moment for the oil to sink down into the case, then stick the dip-stick down in there all the way and check how close to full you are. It'll probably take about another four ounces, or a half-cup, to fill the case. If the thing gave you a full reading with only a pint in it, tip the mower back and forth a bit to release any trapped air down in there and measure again. Do not use the mower with too much oil in it. If you accidently over-fill, you can tip the thing up and dump a little out (very messy), or turn to the oil change procedure in the *Storing Away for Winter* Appendix, and take all the oil out for a second try at filling without over-filling.

On any old mower you just bought, do the oil change procedure just for good measure; see the *Storing Away for Winter* Appendix (page 237).

As for gasoline, if you're about to start a brand-new engine, there's not much to fueling it up. Unscrew (c-cl) the gas cap and take the little cork or metal spacer off the hole if there is one, then pour *fresh* gas (old gas that's been exposed to air for over a month is awful for the engine; it has lost its pep and it gets things gummy) into the tank from a can with a long spout. If the engine is one of those two-cycle ones, you have to mix oil in with it, at a proportion of 16 parts gas to 1 part oil on most models, but 32 to 1 on a few models like the fancy Jacobsen. If you spill a little gas or oil in the process, wipe it up with a rag. You don't want to burn up your brand-new mower, do you?

If you are about to fuel up a secondhand engine and start it for the first time, take a critical look at the gas tank before you put anything in it. Unscrew (c-cl) the gas cap and take off the cork or metal spacer under it if there is one. Is there rust all over the cap and spacer? Look for a little hole or several little holes in the gas cap. Put the top of the cap against your lips (yech, that gas taste) and try blowing through the holes. If the holes are clogged, or if there is rust all over the cap and even down in the tank, *don't* put gas in the tank and try to make the engine go. Turn to the *Fuel Line Clean-Out* paragraph (on page 216), and clean the tank out or replace it and its cap, then come back here to fill up your tank with gas.

Starting

Oil in? Stop spring set? Tank full of fresh clean gas? Good. On most engines you're set to go. But if the engine is one of those that has the tank above the carburetor, look just under the tank, where the fuel line (a thin tube) runs out of the tank, and see if there is a shut-off valve. It will be a lever or a little knob that you turn. Open (c-cl) the valve.

On engines with bowl type carburetors, look for a little button sticking out of the bottom of the bowl on a pole with a spring around it. If there is one of those buttons, or drain valves, as they're called, put a rag under the carb and push the button in for about two or three seconds to let some fuel drain out of the bowl. This will not only make sure that fresh clean fuel is in the bowl, but will also let any water dribble out that has settled to the bottom of the whole fuel system.

Here's a neat prestarting tip: when everything is set, take the engine to a sunny place and let it warm up for a few minutes—make sure that the sun shines on the carburetor—that'll make the gas fumes start floating around excitedly, so that starting the engine will be a breeze. (What? It's a cloudy day? That's a perfect excuse for putting off the job!)

Put the engine on a smooth level place to start it. Put the throttle control at the Choke position, or, in the case of mowers with automatic chokes which have no Choke position, the Fast position. If the mower has a clutch, put it in the Stop position. For added safety with power reel mowers, start the mower with its front against a wall or the garage door, so it can't run away when it starts. If the engine has a primer button (see illustration 66b), press the button and release it a few times, until it makes a wet and squishy sound inside the carburetor.

Stand next to the mower and put the foot that's nearest to it on the deck. Wrap up the rope on a hand-wound starter, or just grab the handle of your rewind starter and pull the rope out briskly, but not violently (see illustration 47). Keep a firm grip on the handle, and if the starter is a rewind one, let the rope draw back in slowly and smoothly without either snapping or stopping as it rewinds. (What's that? You have a crank-and-release spring starter? I *told* you not to get an engine with one of those; wind and release it with extreme caution, and if you have any trouble at all, especially with the release lever or button, *don't* fool with it, just go straight to the *Starter Replacement* procedure, page 191.

If the engine starts right up on the second or third pull, praise the lord, and turn the throttle down from the Choke position to the middle of the Fast position. Shut off the choke by hand, if your engine has a manual one. *Do not run the engine with the choke on!*

If you don't get some action after three or four pulls, change the throttle position from Choke to Slow, and see if it'll start like that. No go? Well, call the engine by its proper unprintable name, and go on to

Problems, General

DAMN THING WON'T START
Before you get too upset, go through a little checklist: Tank full of fresh clean gas? Oil full up? Clutch disengaged? Throttle control on Choke or Start?

When you've taken care of all those questions, still nothing happens when you pull the starter. Why not? Because the engine isn't getting one of the four vital elements that make the bang inside it. Either it isn't turning around (or "cranking over," as they say), or it isn't getting any pressure built up (compression), or it isn't getting fire (a spark from the spark plug) or it isn't getting fuel (the air-gasoline mixture from the carburetor).

You have to first find out which of the four elements is missing, then fix that element (or elements). OK? So do these four quickie tests to find out which element your engine is hurting for. The process of narrowing down the problem is called

TROUBLESHOOTING
Test 1. Pull the starter rope. If it does indeed pull out, watch the little round screen-covered area on the top of the engine (this screen may be just under the starter assembly that the rope goes into). The round screen should spin merrily around as the rope pulls out. If the round screen doesn't turn around, or if the rope won't even pull out, you probably have a very flooded engine,

158

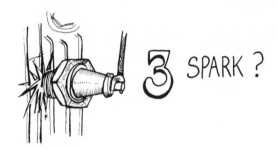

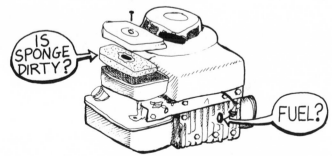

Illustration **47**
The Four Quickie Tests

a jammed blade, or a starter problem. Take the spark plug out (c-cl) with the spark plug socket to check for flooding. If gas pours out of the cylinder, leave the plug out for an hour while you change oil (gas will be in it, too, if you have flooded the engine by turning the mower up on its side—see *Oil Change* in the *Storing Power Mower Away for Winter* Appendix).

On rotary mowers, undo and ground the spark plug wire, then check the blade for grass and gunk clogging things up (see *Housing*, page 132). Check the blade for looseness, too. A loose blade will keep the engine from turning over smoothly on some mowers, so tighten (cl) the blade mounting screw and bolts (see *Blade Loose* in the *Rotary Mower*, page 130). If you check and repair those problems and the mower still doesn't turn over when you pull the starter rope, go to the *Starter* section below and fix the starter (page 168).

On a reel type mower, make double sure the clutch is disengaged, so the engine can turn over without trying to make the mower go forward. If the clutch is disengaged, and the starter still isn't doing its thing right, go to the *Starter* section below (page 168).

Test 2. If the starter is turning the engine over OK, give it a slow pull for the full length of the rope. As you pull, do you feel greater resistance at a couple of points? You should feel the engine get hard to turn over as it goes through its compression stroke (see illustration 44). On a regular four-stroke engine, this will be on every other revolution of the crankshaft. To count the revolutions, watch the round screen that turns around as you pull the starter rope. On most engines, the screen is right under the starter mechanism. On engines with vertical pull starters, the round screen will be up on the top of the engine all by itself. Make a mark on the screen with a felt pen so you can see it come around easily. Do the pulling and counting-the-revolutions-per-compression several times, to make sure you are feeling the right thing. Even

160

on the snazzy new low compression start engines, you can feel that the engine is a bit harder to pull through the compression stroke.

If the engine turns over, but there is no compression, the engine is turning over in its grave. It's dead. Say a little requiem and maybe a few Hail Marys for it, and turn to *Engine Replacement* (page 168). It is not worth it to try and rebuild a lawnmower engine, unless you run a machine shop and have lots of time to wait for parts to come from the factory.

If your engine passed the first two quickie tests, thank your luck; it's not desperately ill. It just has a cold or something. You have to find out which of the two most common maladies the engine is suffering from—no fire, or no fuel.

Test 3. Fire. Take the mower to a fairly dark or shady place. Buy a "test" spark plug, a new plug just like the one in the engine, but with its gap set about .1 inch or so. Much wider than normal, in other words. If you don't know how to set the plug like that, go to the *Plug Change* paragraph of the *Spark Plug* (pages 197–198). Undo the spark plug wire from the plug that's in the engine, and hook it onto the test plug. Put a glove on one hand, and use insulated-handle pliers to hold the spark plug by the white ceramic insulator, with the ground electrode (the L-shaped one that you bend up and down to adjust the gap) or the threads on the side of the plug pressing firmly against some unpainted metal, like maybe the stop spring, if there is one sticking up off the head, or the head itself (the head is the part of the engine the plug screws into), or a head bolt. Set the throttle control or remote control lever on Idle or Slow or even Fast, but *not* on Stop, then have a friend pull the starter rope briskly a couple of times and watch for a spark at the gap between the terminals of the end of the plug, as in illustration 47 (if you get a shock, don't worry, it won't injure you; it just makes you jump like crazy). Does a blue-white or blue and bright orange spark snap across the gap? It should. On four-stroke engines, the spark should jump once every two revolutions, during the compression stroke. On two-stroke engines, the spark should jump once every revolution. Watch the round screen again, like you did when checking for compression, to see if the sparks are jumping regularly on each compression stroke.

If the spark is weak yellow, or if it only jumps occasionally, or if it doesn't jump at all, first move the test plug around to make sure you are getting a good contact with the ground electrode, then see the *Ignition* section (p. 199). If there is a good blue-white spark at the test plug, you should be getting fire at the engine's regular plug, if that plug is OK. And if you haven't slammed the mower blade into a rock or something, thus shearing the flywheel pin (see *Ignition,* page 201), the spark should be happening at the right time.

To check the engine's plug, remove (c-cl) it with the socket wrench and spark plug socket, and do the check as at the beginning of *Spark Plug* (page 194). If you have any doubts about the plug, replace it. Don't try to get by with cleaning it; the cleaning machines they usually have at gas stations use a sand-blasting device, which can leave sand in the recessed part of the plug. This sand can work loose later and ruin all the nice smooth parts inside the engine. So give your engine a treat and install a new plug as in the *Plug Change* (page 197). Fire jumping at a good plug? OK. If the engine still won't start, there's only one possible reason left.

Test 4. Fuel-air mixture. This quickie test may take a little time, depending on what your carburetor and air-cleaner types are.

First check to make sure you have a tank full of fresh clean gas. Don't use gas that's over a month old. In a month's time, gas that's exposed to air will lose all of its most volatile (burnable) elements through evaporation. When you look down into the gas tank to see how much

162

gas is in there, check for foreign matter floating around, like grass or dirt or (aack) rust. If you have left the mower outside for many hot days and cold nights (naughty you), there may be water that has condensed inside the gas tank, and which is hard to see. Those of you who have bowl type carburetors with drain buttons (see illustration 66a), push the drain button and see if water comes out. It will be rusty in color, and it will dribble out, instead of flowing like the gasoline. If you detect or suspect dirt, water, or good old grass-in-the-gas, see *Fuel Line Clean-Out* under the *Fuel-Air System* (page 216).

If your engine is one of those rare birds that have a fuel cut-off valve just under the gas tank (the owner's manuals for those rare bird engines tell you about this cut-off valve), then make sure the valve is open. On any engine that has the gas tank under the carburetor, there will be no cut-off valve.

A few engines have a primer button. It will be a rubber bulb on top of the engine. If you have a primer button, push it a few times in rapid succession. You should hear a squirting noise inside the carburetor—if you don't, see the *Primer* section of the *Fuel-Air System* (page 235).

Do a quick check of the air cleaner. On the top of the air cleaner there will be either a cap with a screw through it (on some models the whole cap unscrews), or a cap with a shape that snaps over the body of the cleaner (see illustrations 58a, b, c). If there is a screw, unscrew (c-cl) it and remove the air cleaner, lifting it straight off the carburetor, being careful not to let any dirt fall down into the carburetor throat. If there is a snap-on cap, unsnap it. Put a rag on the ground and lift out the "element" or insides of the air cleaner. The element may be simply a block of sponge or a paper cylinder, or it may be a metal cup-like thing full of wire matting which sits down in an oil bath. How filthy is the element? If a sponge or paper element is covered with oily gunk, it will starve the engine of air, and the fuel won't burn. This is a *very* common malady. See the *Clean Air Cleaner* paragraph of the *Fuel-Air System* below to fix up the dirty cleaner (page 210).

If you haven't done so yet, take what's left of your air cleaner off the carburetor. Many cleaners just lift off after the cap screw has been removed. Others have screws that hold them to the carburetor. If a metal screen covers the screws, pull it out with the needlenose pliers. Undo (c-cl) and remove these screws, take the cleaner off the carburetor, then start the screws (cl) a few turns back into the carburetor so you can't lose them. If the single cleaner cap screw went into the middle of the carb throat, as on many Briggs and Stratton setups, turn the cap screw back into (cl) its hole a bunch of turns.

OK. You're starting to get at the heart of the matter. Look into the throat of the carb, the hole the air cleaner was over. The air is supposed to go down the throat and mix with the gas inside the carburetor, then go on as a fine burnable mist into the engine. Right at the throat there should be (on almost all engines except those weirdo ones that have primers) a valve that can close it off. It's called the choke valve. Find it in your engine's throat. Ask the thing to say aah, look into the throat, and see if you can see either a round flat plate that can swivel open and closed on an axis (a butterfly valve) or a sliding plate that covers a little doorway. If you're not sure what the choke valve is, move the throttle control (or the choke lever on the carb itself if you don't have a remote control choke) in and out of the Choke position, and watch for a valve opening and closing in the carb throat. On many late-model carbs, there is an automatic choke instead of a Choke position on the throttle. This kind of choke valve should be closed whenever the engine isn't running. Don't be surprised if the choke valve doesn't close all the way. It's a very common malady—kind of like a "stuffy nose" in reverse. It might well be the reason you can't start the damn engine. If the choke valve fails to close all the way when the throttle is in the Choke position, turn to the

Throttle Control Adjustment (page 233) in the *Fuel-Air System* section below. If your Automatic Choke isn't closed, go to the *Fuel Line Clean-Out* (page 216) instead. After you have fixed the choke so it works, try to start the engine again. Still no go? Continue with the rest of Test 4.

Close the choke and pull the starter at least six times in a row, then unscrew (c-cl) the spark plug with the spark plug socket and look for furl moisture all around the end of the plug. It'll collect on that flat circular area where the threads and the ground terminal (the L-shaped one) meet. If there's loads of fuel all over the end of the plug, the engine is flooded. Leave the plug out of its hole for a while, and wipe its business end dry, then put it back in and try starting the engine with the throttle not quite so far toward its Fast or Choke extreme.

If you can't find any trace of fuel on the plug after pulling the starter a bunch of times, then there's something wrong with the fuel half of the fuel-air system. First do the *Fuel Line Clean-Out* (page 216), then, if she still doesn't start, do the *Carburetor Adjustment*. Don't start twiddling around with the carb until you have checked out all other possibilities, though. It's rare that a lawn-mower carburetor, by itself, will get fouled up enough to keep an engine from starting. Much more common are the weak spark at the plug, the choke that ain't choking the throat of the carb, or the clogged or watery fuel supply.

Other Engine Problems

ENGINE STARTS, THEN STOPS

You don't have too much trouble getting the damn thing going, but then it poops out on you after just a few minutes. Nine times out of ten the pin-hole vent in the gas cap is clogged. See the first step of the *Tank Reassembly* (page 224) of the *Fuel Line Clean-Out* in the fuel-air system, below. If that isn't the trouble, you probably have a clogged fuel line (see the *Fuel Line Clean-Out,* page 216), or a maladjusted carburetor (see *Carburetor,* page 230), or a fouling spark plug (see the *Spark Plug Problems,* page 194).

ENGINE SURGES WHEN RUNNING

The engine won't run at the same speed. It goes faster for a few seconds, then slower, then faster again, back and forth. The problem is usually a maladjusted carburetor (see *Carburetor,* page 230), or a messed up throttle (see *Throttle Control,* page 233). If neither of those things solves the problem, the carburetor has internal problems, and should be taken to a pro.

ENGINE SQUEAKS, SCREECHES

When you pull the starter, the engine makes a scraping, squeaking noise. If the engine starts up, this sound progresses up to a shrieking screech. Turn the engine off. Check the edge of the round screen that's around the starter shaft, or on top of the engine (on vertical pull rotary mower engines). The screen, or the flywheel under it, is hitting the blower housing. Loosen (c-cl) the screws that hold the housing to the engine, move the housing a bit so there is equal space all around the screen, then tighten (cl) the housing screws.

BAD VIBRATIONS

The engine shakes like crazy when it's running. First check the blade, if it's a rotary (see page 126, *Blade Sharpening*). The blade may be bent or out of balance. Then check the bolts that hold the engine to the mower. If they're all tight, you probably have a bent crankshaft, especially if you have hit a big rock with a rotary mower. Take the mower to a good shop. Ask them to try to straighten the shaft. If the shaft can't be straightened, you have to replace the whole engine. See *Engine Replacement,* below.

If the cause of the vibration is a big crack in the mower deck, you have no choice but to replace the whole mower—welding never holds up.

ENGINE OVERHEATS

The whole engine starts to smoke and stink after it has
been running awhile, and it feels hot if you get anywhere
near it. *Don't* go on using the mower. Check the blower
housing and flywheel for big clots of grass and junk (see
House Cleaning in the *Breaker Points Overhaul* part of
the *Ignition* section, page 200), then make sure you have
all the parts of the housing in place. The carburetor might
be running lean (see *Carburetor,* page 230), or there may
not be enough oil in the crankcase (check the oil level).
On two-cycle engines, the fuel-oil mix may be off.
Remember that it has to be 16 parts gas to 1 part oil on
most mowers with two-cycle engines. You may be simply
working the mower too hard. Don't use it in grass that's
too deep or wet, and stop it now and then to clean the
housing (see *Housing,* page 133, and *don't* go under that
housing without undoing and grounding the spark plug
wire).

ENGINE LACKS POWER

The thing just doesn't have much get-up-and-go, and it
quits when you put any strain on it. First check for grass
and gunk build-up; on a reel mower, around the cutter bar
and reel blades, on a rotary mower, around the blade
under the housing (undo and ground the spark plug wire
before you start cleaning around the blades). If the engine
is panting out black smoke, check to make sure the choke
is off (*Throttle Control Adjustment,* pages 233–234),
and that the air cleaner is clean (see *Clean Air Cleaner,*
pages 210–214), then try adjusting the carburetor (see
Carburetor Adjustment, page 230). If those things don't
help, do the four quickie tests; your mower engine may
be dirty, or it may be approaching retirement age (see
Engine Replacement).

ENGINE SHOT

The damn thing just won't start or go or do anything. Or
it didn't pass the second quickie test. In either case it's
time for

ENGINE REPLACEMENT

This is an unbelievably simple process. Undo the clamp screw for the remote throttle control if you have one attached to your carburetor (see page 236, *Control Wire Replacement*). Then, on a reel mower, get the belt off the engine pulley. On a rotary mower, do the *Blade Removal* (page 122). Then simply loosen (c-cl) the four bolts that hold the base of the engine to the mower, and lift it off the deck. Make sure your replacement engine is the same size and horsepower as the old one. Have the shop where you buy it put a new pulley or blade hub on the engine shaft, then mount it on the mower with the bolts that held the old engine. Tighten (cl) the bolts thoroughly, hook up the throttle control wire (see *Throttle Control Wire Replacement,* page 236), reset the blade or belt, and you're ready to go.

Starter

Description

The starter turns the engine over to get it going. It makes the crankshaft turn around, in other words. Now, on a little lawnmower engine, it doesn't take much to crank the engine over. A rope that you simply wind around a pulley and pull is plenty. A rewind starter (the kind where a spring pulls the rope back around the pulley after you have drawn the rope out) is more than adequate. A crank-and-release starter, with all of its violent, dangerous tendencies, is a crazy example of overkill that often backfires. And an electric starter, on a lawnmower, is sheer lunacy. Look at it this way. You have to work about ten hours at some job that pays three bucks an hour to pay the extra cost of an electric starter. It takes about ten seconds and really *very* little work to wind and pull the old-fashioned kind of starter. If the engine is in good shape (it will be, if you use this book), you can start the engine with about three pulls. So why get an electric starter? The bugger won't work most of the time anyway. The point of all this harangue is that any engine with a complicated starter will usually have a very simple method designed into it for converting from the troublesome, expensive unit to a more primitive, but also more reliable starting system. So, when you have trouble with your fancy crank-and-release or electric starter, *don't* fix it. Take it off and see if there is a pulley under it that you can wrap the rope around, or holes for mounting a standard rewind rope starter. See *Starter Replacement* (page 191) for details.

If your rope rewind starter isn't working, you can get to its specific problem by just pulling the rope and watching what happens.

If nothing at all happens when you pull the rope, you either have a jammed blade or clutch, or a flooded engine (see quickie Test 1, above), or something stuck in the flywheel (see *Breaker Points Overhaul* and do the *House Cleaning* under *Ignition*, page 200), or you have a jammed starter. If you check the first four possibilities and find that they're OK, go on to the *Jammed Starter* paragraphs below.

If the rope breaks when you pull, go to *Rope and Spring Replacement*, page 181.

If the rope pulls out OK, turning the engine over as it should, but then doesn't wind back up on a rewind starter, or winds back up very slowly, first check to make sure the housing isn't bent and hitting the starter pulley; then, depending on how badly worn and frayed the rope is, go to either the *Rope and Spring Replacement*, or the *Tired Rewind Spring* section (page 181 or 179).

If the rope pulls out and winds up OK, but doesn't turn the engine over as it should, or slips so that the engine only turns occasionally, on a simple hand-wound rope starter, tighten (cl) the big flywheel nut to at least 20 foot-pounds; on a rewind starter, go on to

STARTER CLUTCH SLIPPAGE
(REWIND STARTER)
You pull the old starter rope, and there's all kinds of noise

from the starter, but the engine doesn't turn over, or it turns over very irregularly. The thing that engages the starter with the engine is missing its engagement.

First undo and ground the spark plug wire (see Frontispiece). Then take the whole starter unit off the engine, except on Tecumseh rotary mowers with vertical pull starters. On those, you can get at the works without dismantling anything. But on all horizontal, diagonal, and vertical pull Briggs and Stratton starters (see illustrations 48b, 50), and on all horizontal and diagonal pull starters on Tecumseh, Pincor, Jacobsen, Lawn Boy, and other oddball mower engines (see illustration 51a, b), you just unscrew (c-cl) the three or four screws that hold the starter unit to the rest of the mower, and lift the starter off. On Brigg and Stratton engines, you'll notice that the starter is often held in a big metal case (called the blower housing—see illustration 46) that goes half way around the engine. Don't let that scare you off. Make sure at least two little white nylon bumpers (see illustration 48b) are holding the starter pulley in there, then just undo (c-cl) the three hex-head screws that hold the housing and take the whole thing off the engine. On other Briggs and Stratton engines, a vertical pull starter is held on by two bolts, one of which is hard to get at; you have to use a socket wrench (see *Tools* Appendix) to get it off, or take the air cleaner off and use a regular wrench and loads of time and patience.

When you have the starter off, lay it down on a table with the insides up, but *don't* tamper with those insides yet. The thing that was slipping, the starter clutch, will now be visible. Go to the paragraph that applies to your starter, and fix 'er up.

On *Briggs and Stratton* engines with horizontal or diagonal pull starters, the clutch is that squarish post sticking up on the end of the crankshaft, and the round, covered, bowl-like thing that the squarish post goes down into and which the round screen is held to by four hex-

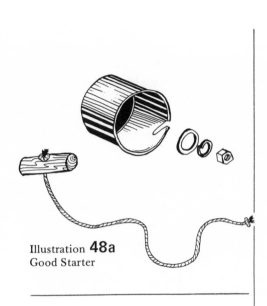

Illustration **48a**
Good Starter

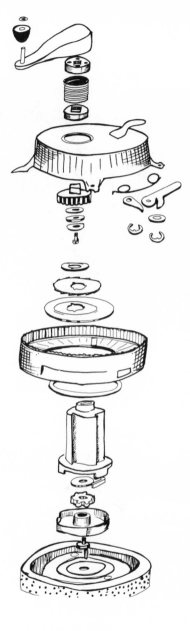

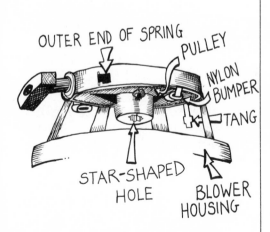

OUTER END OF SPRING

PULLEY

NYLON BUMPER

TANG

STAR-SHAPED HOLE

BLOWER HOUSING

Illustration **48b**
An OK Starter (Rewind)

Illustration **48c**
Bad Starter
(crank-and-release)

head screws (see illustration 49). Remove (c-cl) these four screws and take the screen off the clutch housing. Clean any gunk and grass off the flywheel and the starter clutch. Then have someone hold the flywheel so it can't spin around, or, on a rotary mower, put your foot under the mower via the discharge chute (you *have* grounded the spark plug wire, haven't you?) and push your toe up gently against one end of the rotary blade so the engine shaft can't turn around. When the shaft is held still one way or another, take a small hardwood block and place one corner against one of the little screw hole nubs that stick out from the side of the starter clutch housing for the screen screws. Tap the block with a light hammer in such a way that you tighten (cl) the clutch onto the shaft (see illustration 49). If that clutch has come loose on the shaft, the starter will slip.

If the starter clutch was on good and tight, grab the squarish post and spin it back and forth. If it's sluggish and/or doesn't catch when you spin it clockwise, then its working parts must be either worn down or gunked up. In either case, or if the thing is old and rusty, the best thing to do is to replace the whole unit. On some old units you can take a snap ring off the cover and get into the works for cleaning, but it's not worth the trouble, because you usually have to replace all the working parts anyway. So just take your hardwood block and light hammer, and use the same method you used to tighten (cl) the clutch housing, only this time tap the thing counterclockwise to loosen it, then screw it all the way off the crankshaft (see illustration 49). Leave the washer that's under the starter in place. Take the old clutch to your local friendly mower parts store and get an exact replacement. There are two distinct models, so make sure you get one like yours. The old model has a hole in the top of the squarish post that you can see the end of the shaft through. On the new model, the end of the squarish post is solid. Make sure the cupped washer is on the shaft still. If you took it off, put it back on with the cupped or hollow side toward the flywheel. Thread (cl) your nice new starter clutch onto the driveshaft carefully so it doesn't strip. Tighten (cl) it well with the old hardwood-block-and-hammer treatment, holding the shaft still as before. Don't whack on the block too hard, just keep tapping it until you can see that the clutch isn't going to go any farther.

Put the round screen back in place on the new clutch, and replace (cl) the screws that hold the screen to the clutch. Sight across the top of the flywheel to see if the screen is down flush all the way around its perimeter. If part of the screen has gotten bent so it sticks up, tap it down gently with the hammer so it won't hit the blower housing. If the squarish post on your new clutch has a little word "Top" stamped on the corner, and you're working on a power reel mower, turn the post (c-cl) until the "Top" corner is pointing toward the spark plug, or straight up. Then settle the blower housing and starter into place, wriggling the squarish post a bit if you have to, so it fits into the hole in the starter pulley. Make sure

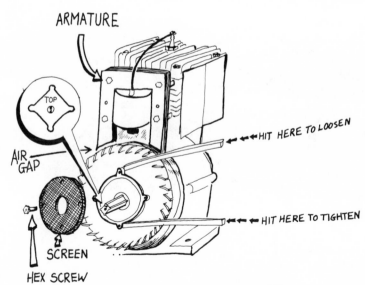

ARMATURE

TOP

AIR GAP

HIT HERE TO LOOSEN

HIT HERE TO TIGHTEN

SCREEN

HEX SCREW

Illustration **49**
Briggs and Stratton Starter Clutch

173

the edges of the housing are overlapping the other shielding on the engine all the way around, then replace (cl) and tighten (cl) the three hex-head screws that hold the housing in place.

On *Briggs and Stratton* engines with vertical pull starters, clutch slippage can be caused by gunk in the starter teeth, or by worn-down teeth, or by a ruined link. When you have removed the starter, hold it so you can look into the oblong hole in its side and watch the white plastic sprocket in there as you slowly pull and release the starter rope. The sprocket should pop up or down on its shaft each time the rope changes direction, and it should spin around smoothly. The teeth of the sprocket should all be intact and free of gunk. If they are dirty, clean them. If they are all sheared off or worn down, simply replace the whole starter—the sprocket can't be bought by itself, and it's much simpler to replace the starter unit than dismantle it anyway.

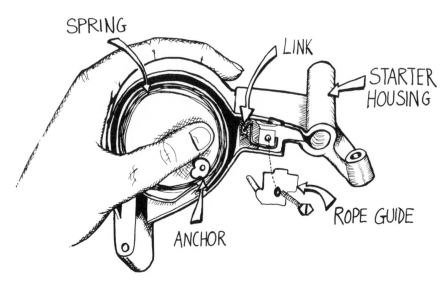

SPRING

LINK

STARTER HOUSING

ROPE GUIDE

ANCHOR

Illustration **50**
Briggs and Stratton Vertical Pull Starter

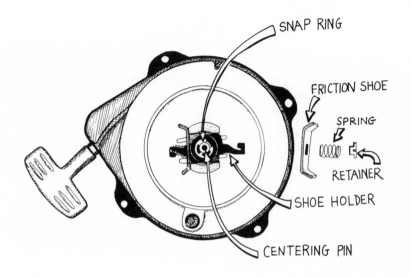

SNAP RING

FRICTION SHOE

SPRING

RETAINER

SHOE HOLDER

CENTERING PIN

Illustration **51a**
Friction Shoe Starter

If the sprocket is in good shape, but doesn't pop up
and down each time the rope changes direction, then take
a close look at the link, that black wire with all the curves
and joints in it (see illustration 50). If the link is all mangled out of shape, or has jumped out of place, go on to
the *Rope and Spring Replacement*, pages 181—191, to dismantle the starter and replace the link.

On *Tecumseh* engines with horizontal or diagonal
pull starters, and on most other engines with horizontal
or diagonal starters, there are two different types of
clutch mechanisms. Look at the starter after you have
taken it off the engine. On the side of the starter that
was closest to the engine, there will be either a complicated shoe and spring setup as in illustration 51a, or a
drum retainer with a blade or "dog" sticking out of it,
as in 51b.

If your engine has a friction shoe starter that's slipping (see illustration 51a), look for gunk and grease around

the shoes and in the cup that's still attached to the engine. Also check the complicated shoe and spring setup, pulling and releasing the starter cord and watching to see if the shoes are spreading out to a long parallelogram when you pull, then retracting to a square when you release the cord. If the friction shoe gismo is all bent out of shape, or if the shoes are obviously worn down or ruined, you can replace them by prying the snap ring off that holds them to the starter shaft, and carefully removing the little parts that are around the shaft, laying them out in the order they come off on a table so you'll remember the order for reassembly. Pay special attention to the friction shoe gismo as it comes off—the L-shaped ends of the plate that holds the shoes have to face the same way when you put the new shoes in. Leave the pulley on the shaft; if you pull it up, it'll let the big mean spring jump out and flail all over the place. Take the whole friction shoe assembly and get an exact replacement. Reassemble the starter with the new shoes in the same position the old ones were in. When you have the snap ring pushed, pried, and cussed back into place, try pulling and releasing the rope again. The shoes should pop away from the center of the starter, making an elongated parallelogram when you pull, and move back toward the center to form a square when you release the rope. Before remounting the starter on the engine, check for a brass pin sticking out of the middle of the starter shaft. This is the centering pin. Is it straight? If it's bent, measure how much of it is sticking out of the shaft, then pull it out with pliers and put it on a flat hard surface. Roll it along and tap it with a hammer so it straightens out. When it's straight, tap it back into the shaft until the same amount of it is sticking out as before, plus about 1/8 inch extra. Now put the starter on the engine so the centering pin is started into its hole in the end of the engine shaft. Start two adjacent mounting screws into their threads (cl) but don't tighten them. Push the starter slowly down onto the engine so the centering pin lines things up. Start the other mounting screws (cl),

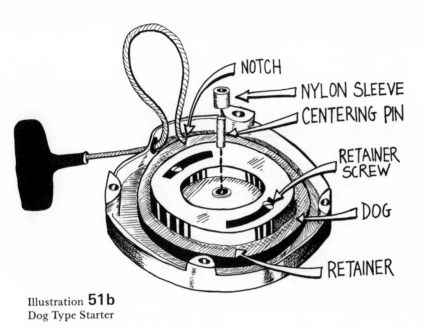

Illustration **51b**
Dog Type Starter

then tighten (cl) them all thoroughly. If the starter still won't turn the engine over as it should, go back to the starter diagnosis section and find out what else is wrong with the system.

If your *Tecumseh* engine has a "dog" type starter clutch as in illustration 51b, you must first remove the brass centering pin and its little nylon sleeve (if the starter has them), then unscrew (c-cl) the screws that hold the retainer on. Take the retainer off and look at the works that hold and operate the dog. If the dog is bent or worn down, or if the spring that pulls it in is shot, or if there is a round metal brake with arms sticking up and the arms are all mangled, observe which way the parts fit in there, then take off the messed-up ones and get replacements. If it's the spring or dog you replace, make sure you put the new one on the way the old one came off. If you have to remove the center screw to get the brake off, make sure you keep the pulley down on the shaft so the spring can't get loose and start flailing around trying to poke your eyes out. Keep all the washers and things that come off the shaft in order too. When reassembling, make double sure all the little springs are in place and that the dog is on the right way so that when you later (*not* now) pull the rope, the dog will pop out and hit the clutch housing. Screw in the center screw (cl) if you took it out, then replace the retainer cup and screw the screw(s) back in (cl) that hold it. Try pulling the rope a few times and watching the dog to make sure you have things together right. Get the centering pin straight by rolling and tapping it with a hammer on a flat hard surface, then set it into its hole in the end of the starter shaft screw. Place the nylon sleeve (if there is one) on the end of the engine shaft, put the starter in place on the engine and just start (cl) two adjacent mounting screws into their threads. Slowly push the centering pin through the nylon sleeve and into the hole in the end of the engine shaft. When the starter is properly centered, start (cl) the remaining mounting screws, then tighten (cl) them all thoroughly. Try the thing out. If you still have problems, go back to the starter diagnosis paragraph again.

If your *Tecumseh* engine with a vertical pull starter has slippage problems, my first suggestion is to buy a whole new starter, the kind that fits on top of the engine. Tecumseh makes it easy to do that. See *Starter Replacement.* If the thing has a bent brake spring, or link (see illustration 50 for the Briggs and Stratton counterpart), but is otherwise clean and in good working order, you can take out (c-cl) the three screws that hold the starter to the engine, pull the starter out a bit, take the brake spring out of its slot on the gear piece, then replace it with a new one. Hold the starter mounting bracket with one hand and pull the rope with the other, just to make sure the new spring pops the gear up and down each time the rope changes direction. Often even with a new spring the starter will act up, especially if it has grease and gunk all over it, or if it has gotten mangled by the old spring. Go to *Starter Replacement* (page 191), as you were told to do in the first place. If the starter works with the new brake spring (link), mount it back on the engine and start the three screws in (cl), but don't tighten them yet. Pull the starter rope gently so that the plastic gear just engages with the gear teeth on the flywheel. Slide the starter mounting bracket up and down until there is at least 1/16 of an inch (that's about a pencil-lead thickness—you can judge it by eye), measured ver- tically, between the end of the starter gear teeth and the deepest part of the flywheel cog that the teeth stick up into. You need that clearance so the starter gear won't get hung up on the flywheel when the engine starts up. When the starter is in the right place, tighten (cl) the mounting screws thoroughly, then try the thing out. Problems? Go to *Starter Replacement* on page 191.

TIRED REWIND SPRING
The starter turns the engine over OK, but then doesn't wind the rope back up again. The engine starts up, and about a foot of rope is still dangling out of the starter and flopping around where it can get caught in the works. First check to make sure the starter isn't just a little sticky.

On all starters but the vertical pull ones, pull out the rope slowly and let it rewind as much as it will. If it catches all the time, even when the rope is just starting back in, the spring may be rusty and sticky or, on a Briggs and Stratton engine, the pulley tangs and bumpers might be bent or ruined (see illustration 48b), or the rope might be wrapping up wrong. Squirt a drop or two of oil up behind the pulley where the spring is, then pull the cord rapidly a few times to spread the oil around. On a Briggs and Stratton engine, bend the tangs so they are like those in illustration 48b, leaving a little extra space between the bumper and the pulley so it can spin freely. Replace any nylon bumpers that are shot. If a tang breaks off as you bend it around, just use the extra one that's right next to it, so nicely supplied by B&S. If, on any starter, the rope bulges out of the pulley in one place as more and more of it winds up, then the rope isn't attached to the pulley correctly. Go to the *Rope and Spring Replacement,* below, and get the rope on right.

When you have eliminated all the little problems that might make your rewind starter sticky, you are left with the possibility of a tired old spring. To tighten the old thing and get some more life out of it, first remove the starter (you don't have to remove a Tecumseh vertical pull starter for this procedure). Loosen (c-cl) and remove the mounting screws that hold the starter to the rest of the engine (on Briggs and Stratton horizontal and diagonal pull starters, you loosen (c-cl) the bolts that hold the whole blower housing on). Take the starter off and lay it down with its top on a table, so you can see the pulley. On most Tecumseh starters, you will see a notch in the pulley (see illustration 51b). To tighten the spring, simply make a loop of rope as in illustration 51b, holding the pulley still with a thumb as you do so, then turn the pulley a full turn tighter, pulling the loop of rope so it passes over the pulley. When the notch is back into the position it started in, take the rope out of it, and see if the pulley will now wind up that rope easily. If the spring is still too loose, take another turn of the pulley as you did before. Don't tighten the thing any more than necessary though, or it'll snap when you pull the rope all the way out.

On Briggs and Stratton engines you can use the same method, even though there isn't any notch. Just pull about a foot of rope out of the pulley as in illustration 51b, using needlenose pliers to start the loop, then turn the pulley a turn tighter, and let it wrap the loop back up. You will have to pass the rope between the pulley and the pulley tangs as you tighten the pulley, so bend the tangs up a bit and tilt the pulley slightly to get the rope around. Remember to bend the tangs back into place when you're done, and *never* let the pulley tilt up so far that the spring can leap out and start flailing its ends at your eyes.

On Tecumseh vertical pull starters, the same loop-and-pulley-tighten method described above can be used. It'll work on Briggs and Stratton vertical pull starters too, if the starter is first removed from the engine by undoing (c-cl) its mounting bolts. Be especially careful with vertical pull starters that you don't over-tighten the spring, though; one turn tighter should be plenty if the starter is in good condition otherwise.

Put the starter back on the mower as per the instructions in the *Starter Replacement* section on page 191.

STARTER JAMMED

You pull the starter rope and nothing happens, and you've checked the engine for flooding and the blade or clutch to see if they were clogged up. Remove the starter from the engine by unscrewing (c-cl) the mounting screws and lifting it off. On Briggs and Stratton engines with horizontal or diagonal pull starters, you have to remove the whole blower housing to get the starter off.

When you have the starter off, look at the pulley and see if the rope has jumped out of it. That's usually the trouble. Pull a loop of the rope out and stuff it all back into the pulley via the notch, or if the rope is hopelessly jammed behind the pulley, turn to *Rope and Spring Replacement* and use that procedure to get the rope back in. If the rope is OK, and the starter housing isn't obviously bent out of shape so bad that the thing can't turn, then the only part that can be causing the trouble is the spring. It must be bent or broken and clogging the works. Go on to

ROPE AND SPRING REPLACEMENT

Your rope and/or spring are either broken or ruined or badly jammed. Both the spring and the rope must be dealt with simultaneously on most engines, so go through the following procedure for your engine whichever problem you have. Each kind of starter has a different procedure, so find the paragraphs that deal with your type.

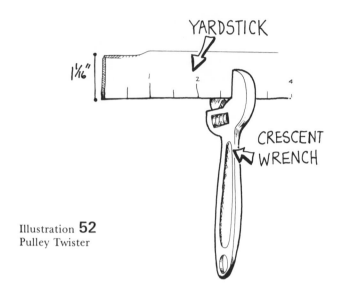

YARDSTICK

CRESCENT WRENCH

1-1/16"

Illustration **52**
Pulley Twister

On *Briggs and Stratton* engines with horizontal or diagonal pull starters, first unscrew (c-cl) the bolts that hold the whole starter-blower housing unit to the engine, then take the unit off the engine and lay it down on its top. Look at the pulley down in the housing; it's the round thing with a knot of rope sticking out of a hole in it. In the middle of the pulley there is a big hole shaped like an eight-pointed star. You are going to need a tool that you can stick in that hole and turn the pulley around. The ideal thing is a bar of ¾ inch square stock, but how many of us have things like that lying around? Take a standard wood yardstick that is 1-1/8 inches wide and whittle one end down to 1-1/16 inches wide with rounded corners; it'll work like a charm (see illustration 52). Don't whittle the stick down too much, or it'll fit loosely in the hole and slip out when you really don't want it to.

If your spring is still intact, take your nice pulley-twister, stick it into the pulley, put a crescent wrench on it for leverage, then twist the pulley so it slacks up on the rope. When you have about 6 inches of slack rope, slide the crescent wrench down the twister until it's inside the blower housing, and you have the thing locked in position. Pull the end of the rope out of the handle and untie the knot or cut it off if it's too tight to untie. Pull the loose end of the rope back through the handle, and use your twister as a brake to let the spring slowly wind up all the rope on the pulley and then go right on turning until there is no spring tension left.

If your rope broke, the spring will have lost its tension already. In fact the spring probably snapped so hard when the rope broke that it too will be broken. Get a firm grip on the end of the spring that sticks out of the housing (see illustration 48b) with a pair of pliers. Move the spring to the part of the hole in the housing that's widest, then try to pull it out. If it comes easily, you can assume that the spring is busted, and pull the whole loose end out. If it resists, don't pull hard on it. Instead, take the pliers and bend up one of the tangs that hold the pulley in (see illustration 48b), then tip the pulley up out of the housing a bit, just enough so you can reach under it. Get ahold of the part of the spring that comes out of the center of the pulley in there quickly, so it doesn't start the whole thing unraveling and flailing around. Then twist and wiggle the pulley around until the inner end of the spring comes undone. Put the pulley aside, and hold the bulk of the spring down in the housing with one hand while you pull the inner end up and out. Work the rest of the spring out, letting just one loop of it ease up at a time, working from the middle to the outside. See illustration 54 to get the general idea. When you have safely removed the whole spring, you can relax a bit. The thing can't take your eye out now. To take the rope out of the pulley, unwind it, then grab the knot that sticks out of the pulley and pull the rest of the rope through the hole. *Get an exact replacement for the rope.* Briggs and Stratton makes nifty ones with a wire sticking out of the inner end to make the pulley-threading job easier. But if you can't get one of those, get a rope that is nylon, woven like the original (not twisted), and the exact same diameter and length as the old one (use the pieces of a broken rope to get the total length). *All* of the properties and characteristics of the new rope have to be the same as those of the old one, or it will act up sooner or later. Make nice clean cuts on the ends of your new rope, then melt the nylon strand ends a bit by heating them with a match. To make the threading process a lot easier, squeeze and shape the ends of the rope with pliers while they are still warm (not hot), thus forming roughly pointed ends, instead of big bulgy ends that will be hard to push through the guide holes in the pulley and the housing.

Threading the rope is a bummer no matter how nice you fixed the ends. Get a long thin screwdriver and an awl to make the job easier. First feed and prod one end of the rope into the pulley from the outside to the hole, as in illustration 53, making sure it is lining up to pull the pulley counterclockwise (from the present point of view), and also making sure that the rope goes inside (toward the center of the pulley) of the little guide post in there if there is one (see the dotted lines on illustration 53). When the end of the rope appears in the hole, either pull the wire or grab the end of the rope with a pair of needle-nose pliers and pull it up out of the hole. Tie a knot in the end of the rope with as little as possible left over, like 1/8 inch or less. Cut the wire off if there was one on the end of a Briggs and Stratton special rope. If the hole on the pulley is big enough (it'll be big enough on pulleys that don't have the guide post), manipulate and pull the knot down into the hole completely. On the small-hole-and-guide-post type pulley, try to work the knot around so the bulk of it is toward the center of the pulley from the hole; that way the knot won't catch on the tangs that hold the pulley in the housing. You can usually see a shiny ring worn onto the dull grey surface of the pulley where the nylon bumpers rub it—make sure the knot doesn't protrude over that shiny ring.

Wrap the rope tightly around the pulley, counter-clockwise with the knot hole toward you. That way it'll

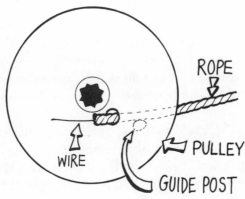

Illustration **53**
Briggs and Stratton
Rope Pulley

pull out clockwise when the pulley is right side up. Stick
the end of the rope in the pulley slot along with the rest
of the rope. If it keeps flobbing out, stick it in there with
a bit of tape. Put a dab of grease on the spring side of the
pulley, and a dab on the inside of the top of the housing;
the spring will spread the two dabs around.

Take the new spring, hold it so the inner end points
counterclockwise (like this ⑥), then stick the inner end
from the outside of the housing through the spring hole
into the inside of the housing. (The housing is still lying
upside down on the ground, isn't it? It should be.)
Lower the pulley down into the housing with the knot
hole up, and tilt it so one edge goes under the tang you
didn't bend up. Now thread the inner end of the spring
into its slot in the pulley so that it comes out of the slot
and goes clockwise around the pulley and off to the hole
in the housing.

Lower the pulley all the way down into the housing
and put the twister into the star-shaped hole. Twist the
pulley counterclockwise with the wrench on the twister,
so that the whole length of the spring is drawn through
the hole in the housing and wound up on the pulley.
When the outer end of the spring comes to the hole in
the housing, make sure its notched end settles firmly into

the narrow part of the spring hole. Then wind the pulley another two turns tighter with the twister, and, being careful now not to let the pulley tip up too high and let all that spring come flailing out, turn the pulley until the outer end of the rope is adjacent to the rope guide hole in the housing. Tip the pulley just enough so you can get an awl or icepick in to the rope end, and pull the end out so it is sticking into the beginning of the guide hole in the housing. Then turn (c-cl) the pulley with the twister to give the rope an inch or so of slack. Use the awl in the space between the pulley and the guide hole (you can slide the pulley away from the guide hole to increase this space) and gently prod the rope through the guide. When the outer end of the rope comes out of the guide, grab it and pull the rope out about 6 inches. Set the twister so the crescent wrench can slide down and rest against the inside of the housing, holding the pulley still. Bend the bent up tang back down so that the pulley can't tip up and let the spring out. Push the outer end of the rope through the handle and tie a knot in it, sticking a bolt or screw through the knot for added safety if you want. Settle the knot and bolt or whatever down into the handle and take the twister gismo off the pulley. Try the starter out. If the spring or rope is backwards, go through the procedure again and straighten things out. If the starter works OK, check to make sure the "Top" mark on the starter clutch (see illustration 49) points toward the spark plug, then slide the blower housing and starter back on the mower and screw the mounting bolts back in (cl) firmly. If the starter still has troubles turning the engine over, go back to the *Starter Description* and find out what else is wrong (page 168).

Rope and spring replacement on a *Briggs and Stratton* engine with a vertical pull starter begins with removing the starter. Loosen (c-cl) the hex-head screws that hold the starter to the engine. One of these screws is hard to get at, so you have to either use a socket tool with a two-inch extension (see *Tools* Appendix), or take off the air cleaner, then loosen (c-cl) the bugger just a bit at a time with a box or open-end wrench.

If the rope and spring are still both in one piece, release the tension on the spring. Pull out the rope about 6 inches, then hold the cover that says Caution on it still with your thumb and draw that 6 inches of slack rope back to form a loop like the one in illustration 51b. Now let the spring turn the pulley so that the loop of rope passes over it. Let the pulley go around and around that way until all the tension is out of the spring, and the pulley just sits still. If the spring and/or rope broke, you obviously don't have to do this step.

With the spring tension removed, you can take the spring cover off with only a minimum of danger. Stick a screwdriver between the lip of the cover and the rest of the pulley and twist the blade so that the cover pops up. You may have to do this in a couple of places around the edge of the cover before it comes all the way off. When it does come loose, take it off slowly, and put your hand over the spring quickly, to keep the nasty bugger from jumping out at you. Push all of the spring down as far as it will go in its container. Then hold it in there with one hand while you loosen (c-cl) and remove the center screw with the hex head that goes through the middle of the pulley. It's easiest to loosen this screw with a socket tool, but the job can be managed with an open-end wrench and a lot of patience. Take it easy, whichever way you loosen (c-cl) the screw, and make sure you never let loops of the spring start warping up out of the container; once it starts, there's no stopping it! Take the screw all the way out and let the spring push the inner spring retainer over so it rests against the other coils of the spring. Put the cover right back over the spring if the spring is intact. If the spring is broken, hold the thumb of one hand over it, and remove the coils one at a time from the inside end to the outside end, keeping your hands in the positions shown in illustration 54.

Spring either covered or removed? Good. If the rope is in one piece, pull the handle apart, take the knot out and untie it (an awl or icepick, pushed between the loops of the knot, often helps if you take care not to stick yourself) and take the handle off the end of the rope.

Loosen (c-cl) and remove the rope guide screw (see illustration 50), and take the rope guide off. This will free up the link, that little L-shaped wire that's under the guide. Now you can pull the pulley and gear up out of the starter housing.

If you are replacing the rope, unwind the old one, then prod the knot up out of its hole with an awl or icepick and pull it with a pair of needlenose pliers. Put the pieces of old rope together and get a new rope that is the *exact* same diameter and length as the old one, and that has the same sort of weave of the nylon strands. Accept no substitute. Melt the ends of the strands of the new rope with a match so they won't fray, and squeeze them with pliers or something while they are still warm so they come out pointed instead of all bulgy at the tips. Push the inner end into the pulley and through its hole with the help of an awl, then grab the end with needlenose pliers and pull it through the hole and out again so you can tie a single overhand knot right near the end. Pull the knot very tight, and make sure no more than 1/8 inch of extra rope is sticking out of the knot. Draw the knot down into its little recessed hole, using the awl again if necessary to manipulate the knot around until it seats completely. Move the starter gear up and down on its spiral to make sure the knot isn't in the way. Hold the pulley with the spring retainer end toward you, and wrap the rope clockwise around the pulley. Wrap it tightly, and all the way until the end can be stuck in out of the way.

If you have to replace the spring, now is the time to do it. Start by hooking the outer end in its slot. Then hold the retainer with the thumb of one hand over the part of the spring you have already placed in the retainer, and feed the rest of the spring in, turning the retainer around

188

and around as you go (see illustration 54). Make sure at all times that the spring in the retainer is pushed all the way in and held there by that thumb. When the whole spring is in place, get the inner end retainer and stick the inner end of the spring into its hole as in illustration 50. Put the cover over the spring, so the bugger can't try to take revenge for being cooped up in there.

Check the link. Does it have any extra bends or curves? Does it slip around the slot in the gear piece easily? Replace it if it is at all suspect. Getting the pieces together is a bit like a Chinese puzzle, but with some patience and pushing and pulling, it can be done. If the link won't slip in the slot in the gear because the slot is all messed up, you have to replace the whole plastic shooting match. The individual parts are too hard to come by, and the new models can't be dismantled at all.

If the link is OK, put it back in place as you slide the whole pulley and gear unit down into the starter housing (see illustration 50). Replace the rope guide right away so the L end of the link can't fall down into the works. Put the rope guide screw into its hole and tighten (cl) it all the way.

Turn the pulley until you can see the end of the rope right next to the rope guide. Pull the end out about 6 inches and feed it under the rope guide and around that tiny pulley and on out of the hole in the housing. The awl may come in handy at this point. Thread the end

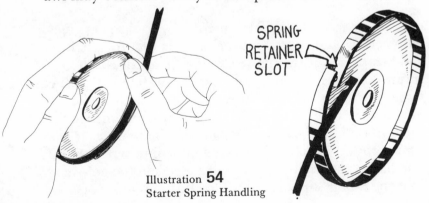

SPRING
RETAINER
SLOT

Illustration **54**
Starter Spring Handling

through the outer handle part and then the inner handle part. Tie a knot in the end and pull the handle parts together over the knot. Turn the starter pulley counter-clockwise so that the rope winds back up all the way until the handle hits the starter housing. Hold the pulley in that position, and pry the spring cover off again. Hold the spring in with the old thumb, just like before, and screw the hex head screw in (cl) through the inner spring retainer, all the way. Tighten it thoroughly, with a socket if you can get one; any looseness at all will release the tension of the spring later.

Replace the spring cover again, and make a loop of extra rope between the rope guide and the pulley, like in illustration 51 b. Grab the part of that loop that is closest to the pulley and pull the pulley around clockwise by the rope two full turns, allowing the loop of extra rope to pass over the spring cover each time. This will tighten the spring just enough. Try the starter out. The gear should pop up or down each time the rope changes direction, and the spring should draw the rope back onto the pulley smartly. Problems? Go back over the procedure, or back to the *Starter Description* if needed. If everything is cooking the way it should, put the starter unit back on the engine and replace (cl) the two hex-head screws that hold it on. Put the air cleaner back in place if you took it off to get at the hard-to-reach starter mounting screw, and you're all ready to start the engine.

Rope and spring replacement on *Tecumseh* engines with vertical pull starters is the same as that for the Briggs and Stratton unit, with a few minor differences. The spring cover is held on by two screws (unscrew, c-cl, them to get the cover off, and screw them back in, cl, whenever you put the cover on, even if it's just for a moment). Also, the link isn't held by the rope guide, which makes it simple to work on. Unfortunately, the link is notoriously unreliable, especially if grease or oil gets in the groove that the link is supposed to slide in. If you have lots of trouble with grass and grease gumming up your link so it gets all bent out of shape, consider getting a whole new starter, maybe even a regular old horizontal pull one (see *Starter Replacement*). If you can get the vertical pull starter to work, be careful to mount it correctly on the engine as in the last part of the Tecumseh *Starter Slippage* discussion above.

Rope and spring replacement for all other various horizontal and vertical pull starters is a pain in the ass. It can also be very painful to the fingers, because the springs are almost impossible to get in and out of their retainers without at least one flailing accident. So don't fiddle with these starters, especially the crank-and-release ones (I've *told* you not to get close to them, and I mean it; they have huge springs with homicidal tendencies). If you have a broken spring and/or rope, just replace the whole starter. It'll cost you about ten bucks, but it'll save you the loss of the fingers on both hands, and possibly the loss of sight in one or both eyes. Ten bucks for all that is the cheapest health insurance you'll ever see, brother. See *Starter Replacement,* below, to be certain to get your dividends.

STARTER REPLACEMENT
Your starter is obviously ruined, or you have been sent here from some other procedure which was too hairy.

Starter replacement on *Briggs and Stratton* engines with horizontal and diagonal pull rewind starters requires loosening (c-cl) the two or three screws that hold the blower housing (the metal case that goes around the starter and the engine—see illustration 46). Remove the screws and take the whole works off. Take it all down to your local mower parts outlet and get an exact replacement. When you start to put the new starter on the engine, look at the end of the starter clutch and make sure the word "Top" is pointing toward the spark plug as in illustration 49. Then slide the housing and starter into place, making sure the housing is overlapping the other metal shields at all points. Tighten (cl) the mounting screws thoroughly, and you are set to go.

Starter replacement on *Briggs and Stratton* vertical pull starters is even simpler. Just unscrew (c-cl) the two mounting screws (one of those is hard to get at—use a socket wrench, or take the air cleaner off to get at it). Take the old starter with you to make sure you get a new one that's the same. Tighten (cl) the mounting screws thoroughly, especially the hard-to-get-at one, when remounting the new starter. Replace the air cleaner, if you took it off, and you're all set.

Starter replacement on *Tecumseh* engines with horizontal and diagonal pull rewind starters is wonderfully simple. Just unscrew (c-cl) the four mounting screws, pull the old starter off and take it with you to get a replacement. Some of the starters are interchangeable with others, but not all can be exchanged. Make sure you get a new starter that is designed to fit the clutch housing on the mower—some housings have teeth, others are smooth. If the new starter has a brass centering pin, push it into the starter shaft the appropriate amount (the instruction sheet with the starter or the shop can tell you how much for each type), then put the starter in place and just start (cl) two adjacent mounting screws in their threads. Press the starter down gently so that the centering pin guides the starter into place. Start (cl) the remaining screws in the threads, and tighten (cl) all of them well. That's all there is to it!

Starter replacement on *Tecumseh* engines with vertical pull starters can be done two ways: you can just replace the starter you have, or you can put a simpler, more reliable horizontal pull starter on top of the engine. I strongly recommend the latter route, if the mower has the four screw holes for the top-mounted horizontal pull starter. It makes a more reliable system (see next paragraph below).

But if your mower has no way to attach a horizontal pull starter, you have to put a replacement vertical pull starter back on. Just make sure you place the new one properly (see the last paragraph of the *Starter Slippage* section above). You have to untie the knot in the handle end of the cord, pull the handle off, and thread that end of the rope through the guide hole in the mower housing. Then put the handle back on like it was, tie the knot again, and you're all set.

If your *Tecumseh* mower is made so that it can be switched over from a vertical pull starter to the old faithful horizontal pull starter, praise the lord! Take off the old starter, cutting the rope if it isn't broken. Pry off the little round cap in the middle of the round screen on the top of the engine, then hold the blade so the engine shaft can't turn and unscrew (c-cl on almost all models, but cl on a few) the big flywheel nut with a socket wrench. Take the nut off and the screen mount that's under it too. Now get your nice new horizontal pull starter and put the clutch housing piece down around the engine shaft and tighten (cl on most models) the big flywheel nut back on good and tight (30 foot-pounds).

Mount the new starter, placing the brass centering pin in the starter shaft if there is one, then just starting (cl) two adjacent mounting screws (you may have to buy these if the screws that were there before were the wrong length), and pushing the starter down gently so the centering pin lines things up. Start (cl) the remaining screws when the starter is in place, then tighten (cl) all of the screws thoroughly.

To replace a *crank-and-release* starter of any brand, take the four mounting screws off and throw the damn thing away. Get a rewind pull starter that'll fit the hub of your old crank-and-release one. For *Briggs and Stratton* people, this means buying a whole new blower housing (which doesn't cost too much), and following the procedure for replacing a horizontal pull starter. *Tecumseh* owners are in luck—they can simply use the wind-up pulley that is under the crank-and-release starter, and start their mower in the most reliable old-fashioned way. If they want to get a rewind starter, though, they can, and then just follow the procedure in the two paragraphs directly above to mount their new starter.

Ignition

Description

Fire, as they call it in the trade. The electrical generator, coil, and spark plug that are supposed to deliver the spark to the compressed fuel and air mixture in order to start the stuff burning in the cylinder.

If you do quickie test 3 and don't get a good spark at the test plug, go right to the *Breaker Points* section below. If the spark is a good strong blue one, and you want to make sure your engine's spark plug is OK, go on to

Spark Plug

Description

You know, the thing with the white porcelain collar that sticks out of the top or one end of the engine (see illustration 55).

To check a plug, take the wire off the terminal, then put the special plug socket on the plug and use the ratchet handle to remove (c-cl) the plug. If the engine has been on, leave the plug alone for a while so it can cool down. Then take a look at the tip of the thing. Orient yourself with the names of the different parts marked on the normal plug in illustration 55. Check the ceramic insulator for cracks, and replace any plug that has even a hint of a crack. Then determine if the plug looks more like

COLD
FOULING

OVER-
HEATING

TERMINAL

CERAMIC
INSULATOR

METAL
SHELL

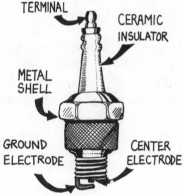

GROUND
ELECTRODE

CENTER
ELECTRODE

WET
FOULING

NORMAL

Illustration **55**
Spark Plug Analysis

the normal one or one of the fouled ones. For each kind
of fouling there are a number of different possible reasons,
each of which must be checked out and repaired if necessary, in addition to following the *Plug Change* procedure
below.

COLD FOULING
The plug tip looks like it is completely covered with a
very thin film of fine black powder. In extreme cases the
film may be wet with fuel, especially if you have just
pulled the starter a bunch of times. Cold fouling is very
common, and shouldn't be worried about if it isn't so

bad that you can't see the white or orange of the part of the ceramic insulator that's around the end of the center electrode. The problem is usually due to the use of the wrong type spark plug, or an improperly gapped plug (see *Plug Change*), or by a clogged air cleaner (clean it out), or by a carburetor that's adjusted too rich or running with the choke on all the time (see *Carburetor Adjustment* and *Throttle Control Adjustment* on pages 230 233), or a poor connection of the spark plug wire and the terminal (tighten the clip on the end of the wire with a pair of pliers if needed, to get a tight fit on the terminal), or too much idling and running the engine with no load on it (don't run the engine unless you are using the mower).

OVERHEATING
The tip of the plug looks like it's melting itself away. The ground electrode will be thinner than it should be, the ceramic insulator will be either cracked or covered with a baked-on black crust, and the whole tip of the plug will look like it's just been in a blast furnace. The trouble might be due to a loose plug (tighten, cl, the new plug to 20 foot-pounds when you put it in with the socket wrench), or the carburetor may be adjusted too lean (see *Carburetor Adjustment* under *Fuel-Air System* page 230), or air may be leaking in to the fuel-air system (check to make sure the air cleaner and carburetor mounting bolts are tight, and that the gaskets are in place and in one piece), or by a clogged and filthy cooling system (if the mower has a lot of clippings and gunk all over it, go to the *Breaker Points Overhaul* and do the *House Cleaning* procedure on page 200).

WET FOULING
The entire tip of the plug is covered by a film of oily, black, glistening glop. Baaad news! Oil is leaking into the cylinder somehow. The rings and/or valves are probably shot. You can do the *Plug Change,* and see how she goes,

but the engine is on its last legs. Some old putt-putts will go on for quite a while like that, but don't count on it.

PLUG CHANGE

Your plug had one of the symptoms above, or you are doing the spring checkup and are replacing the plug for good measure. Always use the correct-size spark plug socket and a socket wrench to remove or install a plug. That way you'll get the plug in and out without cracking or breaking its ceramic insulator. When you have the old plug out and have analyzed it, take it and your owner's manual for the engine, if you have one, and go to the nearest good mower shop or small engine shop. Get either the exact same plug you had before (as long as you're sure it was the factory-installed plug), or one recommended by the owner's manual. Don't take a substitute under an unknown brand name of plug unless you are sure you can trust the judgment of the guy who tells you it's an exact substitute. The safest route is to just keep putting the same plug in the engine that the factory did. They knew what the engine needed.

Get your spark plug gapper out (see *Tools* Appendix) and see if the plug was preset to .030 inch. You should check the owner's manual to make sure .030 is right for your engine. It is on Briggs and Stratton and Tecumseh. Usually the plugs are preset with a gap that's too large. Push the end of the plug against something metal, like the engine block, to make the ground electrode (the L-shaped one) bend toward the center electrode a little at a time. That's some trick. Most of the time, when you try to move it a little bit, you push and push and nothing happens, then you get mad and really push, and the ground electrode bends all the way in and hits the center one. Ain't that the way? Well, don't fret; just bend the ground electrode away from the center one. Stick one of the little L-shaped appendages on the gapper (whichever one you can get under the edge of the ground electrode out near the tip), and pry up. The prying up of the ground electrode is much more controllable than the pushing down process, you'll find. Get the ground electrode bent in such a way that it leaves just enough space to push the .030 inch wire between itself and the center electrode.

Start turning (cl) the new plug into its hole with your bare hands, slowly and carefully; the metal of the plug is harder than the soft aluminum alloy of the engine block, so the threads are easy to strip. If it is at all hard to thread it (cl), take it back out and start again, making sure that you have the plug lined up straight in the hole. Tighten (cl) the plug thoroughly (20 foot-pounds). Attach the wire to the terminal. Was it easy to slip it on, or did you have to push it until it snapped firmly into place? If the wire end clip just slid on and is loose, take it off and squeeze the clip a little with a pair of pliers so that it will fit tightly over the terminal.

Breaker Points

Description

The breaker points, deep inside the engine, control when the spark is delivered to the spark plug. The way in which they control and help to generate the sudden spurt of 20,000 volts that makes the spark is pretty complicated, and it often even strikes me as incomprehensible magic; collapsing fields and switching poles and all that. But we don't need to understand it if we can figure out how to make it work.

IGNITION SHOT
You aren't getting any spark at the test plug used in quickie Test 3. First of all, check the spark plug wire for places where all the insulation may be worn away. If the wire is grounding on the engine, the plug won't deliver any spark. If the engine has a Stop position on the throttle, find the brass stop switch blade (see the *Prestart Preparations* section on stop mechanisms for orientation) and follow the wire that is attached to the stop switch back

to where it disappears into the engine. If this wire is frayed or worn away so that it grounds on the engine, the spark will not make it to the plug. Tape over a grounding spark plug or stop switch wire, and try for the spark on the test plug again. Check to make sure you don't have the throttle control on the Stop or Off position, too, as this will ground the spark very nicely too. When you have eliminated all simple possibilities of grounding on the outside of the engine, you are left with the necessity of doing a complete

BREAKER POINTS OVERHAUL

Before you can overhaul the points, you have to get in to them. This is an adventure in itself. Start by removing any plastic or metal cover over the top of a rotary mower engine.

Next, on rotary mowers with Tecumseh engines, drain the gas tank with a siphon (see the *Blade Removal* paragraph of the *Blade* section in the Rotary Mower chapter, pages 122–123). Remove the gas tank from its slots on the blower housing and pull it off its fuel line.

On any mower that has a gas tank that's an integral part of the blower housing, siphon all the gas out of the tank as above, and undo the fuel line so it won't hang you up later on.

On all mowers, remove the spark plug wire from any guide clamp that holds it to the blower housing (the big shield that covers half the engine—see illustration 46). Then undo (c-cl) the screws that hold the blower housing to the engine. Some of these screws may be hard to find (on Briggs and Stratton engines with vertical pull starters, you have to remove the starter to get at one of the housing screws), but get all of them out, then lift the blower housing (and the starter, if the two are together) off the engine. Turn the housing upside down and put all the screws in it so you don't lose any.

Underneath you will see the flywheel and the finned cylinder of the engine as in illustration 56. Take a look at those parts. Are they covered with filth and grass clippings? If so, you need to do a little

HOUSE CLEANING

If the cooling apparatus has a lot of grass clippings, dirt, or grassy gunk on it, clean the parts off *before* you do the breaker points overhaul. That way you won't get dirt on the points. Take a wire brush and give the flywheel and the cooling fins a good brushing. Wipe off greasy gunk with a rag when you're done brushing, and leave the whole area clean and free of obstructions. By the way, *never* run the engine without the blower housing. It will heat up and explode. Literally.

Engine all cleaned off? Good. Look at the shaft sticking up in the center of the flywheel. This shaft will have either a big nut around it holding the flywheel down, or a starter clutch (on Briggs and Stratton engines, as in illustration 49). Check to make sure you have undone and grounded the spark plug wire (see Frontispiece), then hold the shaft still either by holding the blade (on rotary mowers), or by pinning the flywheel as in illustration 39 or 29d. Get a tool that will fit the shaft and the nut to loosen the flywheel holder-downer.

On *Tecumseh* engines this will be an 11/16 inch regular socket, and the nut will loosen if you turn it in the opposite direction from the direction that the shaft rotates when the engine is running (the engines usually run clockwise, so you loosen counterclockwise).

On *Briggs and Stratton* engines with a big nut on the shaft, you need either a 1/2 inch, a 5/8 inch, or a 15/16 inch *deep* socket. This may call for a trip to a tool shop for just that one socket, but there's no other way to do it. While you're at the shop get a points file, sealer, and a spark plug gapping tool (see *Tools* Appendix) so you'll be all set to do the overhaul. The nut will loosen counterclockwise on all engines except those with a ½ inch nut. Those loosen clockwise, just to make things interesting.

On *Briggs and Stratton* engines with a starter clutch holding the flywheel, remove (c-cl) the four little screws that hold the round screen to the clutch housing, then set a block of hardwood in the loosening position against one of the screw hole nubs on the starter clutch housing as in illustration 49. The starter clutch loosens counter-clockwise on all models. Once you have the thing off, start (cl) the little screws back into their holes so you don't lose any of them.

On other engines you may have to get different size sockets and just try loosening the nut first counter-clockwise, and if that doesn't work, clockwise.

When you have the nut off the flywheel, look for a washer around the shaft. This washer is often a cupped or bowl-shaped one. As you take the washer off, notice that the cupped or hollow side is toward the flywheel. Remember that so you are sure to put it back on the right way later.

The flywheel is stuck on the shaft with a key or shear-pin. You can see the end of the key if you look where the washer was around the shaft; there will be a square cutout in the flywheel, and the end of the key will be in that square. Notice how much the end of the key is either sunk down into that square cutout, or sticking up out of it. It should be very near to flush with the surface of the flywheel. You'll want to try to get it like that during reassembly later. If the key or shear-pin is all mashed so the flywheel has slipped, *that's* why the engine wouldn't start. Make a note to get a new key, and go on with the overhaul.

To loosen the flywheel from the shaft, get a flat fishing weight out of your or your neighbor's fishing box, and put it on the end of the shaft, holding it in place by its wire loop with a pair of vise grips as in illustration 56. Then have a friend stick a big screwdriver under the fly-wheel as in the same illustration and pry up firmly but not violently, as you hit the lead weight just as firmly

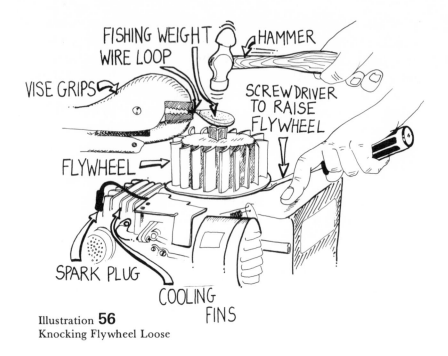

FISHING WEIGHT
WIRE LOOP

HAMMER

VISE GRIPS

SCREWDRIVER
TO RAISE
FLYWHEEL

FLYWHEEL

SPARK PLUG

COOLING
FINS

Illustration **56**
Knocking Flywheel Loose

but nonviolently. If a couple of good whacks and prying
doesn't loosen the flywheel, rotate it 180 degrees and do
the pry-and-whack routine again. Make sure the screwdriver is prying up on the edge of the flywheel; on some
engines, there is stuff under the flywheel that the screwdriver can hit instead of the edge of the wheel itself.
When the wheel comes loose, wiggle and pull it off the
shaft, turn it upside down, put the key in it, and set it
somewhere safe where it won't get stepped on. The fins
of the flywheel are easily broken. If any of the lead from
the fishing weight got mashed down into the hole in the
end of a Tecumseh engine shaft, pick it out with an awl
or ice pick, or drill it out with an electric drill.

You are finally ready to go to work on the breaker
points. Loosen (c-cl) and remove the small hex-head
screws that hold the tin points cover over the points.
Remove the cover very gingerly, pulling harder on the
parts that are held down by sealer (that brown glue stuff

around the holes under the cover where the wires come out). You don't want to bend the cover, because it has to fit tightly in order to keep dust away from the points, which must be kept absolutely clean.

Look at the points. Turn the engine over a few times (turn the blade of a rotary mower, or turn the pulley on a reel type mower—you can take the spark plug out, c-cl, to make the turning easier). Notice that the points close together and move apart as the shaft goes around. They do this about 3,000 times a minute when the engine is running full speed, so they have to work right.

First they have to be clean. If the round surfaces of the points, the surfaces that touch each other, are black and covered with oil, or if there is a little smudge of spattered oil on the metal casing behind the points (see illustration 57a), you have to clean all that gunk off so the points can make a good contact again. If the gunk is spread all over the whole points setup, take the mower to a shop for a points overhaul—it needs some special bushing work that goes over your head. If the points aren't too dirty, take a popsicle stick or a tongue depressor or some small flat stick like that, and wrap a piece of clean, non-raveling cloth around the end. Dip it in kerosene or, if you can get it, rubbing alcohol, and mop all around the points, then clean the points themselves thoroughly. When you have gotten all the gunk off, there still may be a carbonized layer of crud on the meeting surfaces of the points. Get a points file like the one in illustration 57c and slide it between the points. Push the movable point in against the file with one finger, then move the file up and down in short, even strokes so that the crud gets scraped off, but the file doesn't come out from between the points or twist between them and file unevenly. Mop up any flakes of crud or filings that come loose with the popsicle-stick-rag cleaner.

Turn the shaft so that the clean points are closed firmly together. Are two smooth surfaces meeting? Or is there a pit or crater-like hole in one of the points, and a little ragged built-up mound on the other one? If there is a pit or a mound, put the points file between the points as in illustration 57b, press the movable point against the file with one finger, and slide the file up and down in short even strokes until the points are smooth and flush when you let them close together.

GAPPING THE POINTS

When you have clean, smooth points that meet well when they close, turn the engine shaft again until the points are as far apart as they get. This may take some turning back and forth of the shaft. Make sure you do have the gap between the points as wide as possible. Then slip in a .020 inch feeler gauge (like in illustration 57a), or even better, the .020 inch wire on a spark plug gauge between the points. The gauge should slip through, making contact on both points without pushing them apart at all. Look very closely at the movable point as the gauge slips in, and see if it moves at all. If the gauge has to move the points apart to fit in, or if the gauge fits between the points without hitting both, you have to loosen (c-cl) the adjusting screw just enough to move the movable point, change the gap as shown in illustrations 57a, b, and c, then tighten up (cl) the adjusting screw. Check the gap again with the gauge after the adjusting screw is tight. Sometimes the gap changes while you are tightening (cl) the screw. Repeat the whole adjusting procedure if you have to; the gap between the points is very important, and must be accurate. A nifty trick to use if you have a lot of trouble gapping is to adjust the gap a little narrow (the gauge will push the points apart just a bit), then use the points file to file the points off a little at a time until the gap is exact. Use the old popsicle-stick-rag mop to clean up any filings.

When you finally have the points gapped accurately, do a final cleanup all around and between them. Then get a tube of Permatex No. 2 sealer, or some other sealer

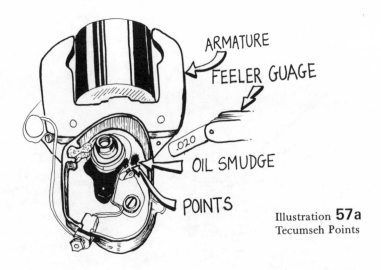

ARMATURE

FEELER GUAGE

OIL SMUDGE

POINTS

Illustration **57a**
Tecumseh Points

that is made for the same applications as Permatex No. 2,
and put a little glob around the wires that go out under
the metal cap. On some models, the wires go through
rubber-sealed holes, but on most you have to do the
sealing yourself.

Put the tin cover back on and push it gently down
over the points housing. Make sure the thing fits snug all
around the edges. If it's bent so it doesn't go on right,
you can take it off and try to straighten it with your bare
hands, but it's better to just replace the cover so you can
be sure no dust and grime get into the points. When the
nice straight cover is down snug over the points, make
sure it is sealing off the wire hole, too, whether you have
sealer or a rubber gasket around the wires.

Screw in (cl) the hex-head cover screws and tighten
them (cl) well, but be careful not to torque (twist) so
hard on them that they strip out the threads in the soft
aluminum block of the engine.

Before you put the flywheel back on the shaft, do
a little test to make sure the flywheel magnets are still
OK. Turn the flywheel upside down if you haven't
already, and lay it on a table with the fins down. Take
a screwdriver and hold it by the end of the handle so that
the end of the blade hangs down an inch away from the

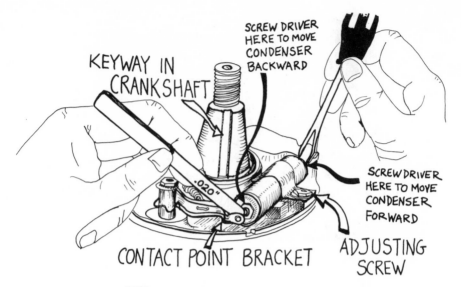

KEYWAY IN CRANKSHAFT

SCREW DRIVER HERE TO MOVE CONDENSER BACKWARD

.020"

SCREW DRIVER HERE TO MOVE CONDENSER FORWARD

CONTACT POINT BRACKET

ADJUSTING SCREW

Illustration **57b**   Briggs and Stratton Points

magnets. On some engines (Tecumseh, for instance) the magnets are on the inside of the flywheel, on others they are on the outer surface of the wheel. You can tell where the magnets are on the wheel because they are shiny, or, if the thing has been sitting out in the rain, rusty. If the magnets are dead, get a replacement flywheel from a good mower shop—take the old wheel and the model number of the engine to the shop and make sure you get just the same type flywheel.

If the magnets are rusty, get some emery paper and sand off the rust. Find the coil armature (the two arms of layered metal and brown insulator that stick out from the big coil that the spark plug wire goes to; the arms pass closer to the flywheel when it is in place—see illustration 49 for the Briggs and Stratton, illustration 57a for Tecumseh) and sand the ends of them to clean off the rust on the part that passes close to the magnets. Then make a promise to your good old mower that you won't ever leave it out in the rain or in some damp old dingy shed again. Keep the mower in a dry place and you won't have any ignition problems caused by rust.

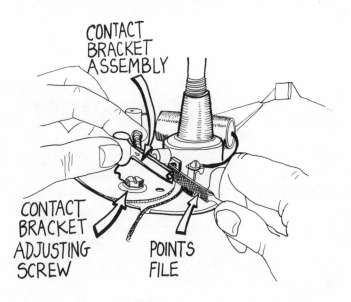

CONTACT BRACKET ASSEMBLY

CONTACT BRACKET ADJUSTING SCREW

POINTS FILE

Illustration **57c**   Briggs and Stratton Points Filing

Check the wires now, too, for any worn places that might cause shorts. Wrap electrician's tape around any bare wire, then push the wires in so the flywheel can't rub against them.

Flywheel, armature, and wires AOK? Good. If the key (shear-pin) is mashed or ruined, get a new one. If you use the mower for rough, heavy-duty cutting and are liable to be hitting rocks and things, you might put an aluminum key in; it will shear off easily if the blade whacks something, thus saving the shaft from bending or the blade from self-destructing. It'll mean more breaker points overhauls, but *much* less expense.

Stick the key into its slot in the engine shaft. On reel mowers, you can turn the shaft around until the slot is on top, then the key will just rest in the slot. On rotary mowers, if the key keeps sliding down and out of the slot, turn the key so that a different side fits into the slot, or flip it end for end and put it into the slot, until you find a way to stick it in so it stays put. The key should be placed in the part of the slot nearest to the end of the shaft—that way, when you push the flywheel down into place, the key will wind up with its end flush with the top (or outer) surface of the flywheel.

Hold the flywheel over the end of the engine shaft with the fins away from the engine, then rotate the wheel until the square cutout is lined up with the key on the engine shaft. Slide the wheel down over the shaft gently, wiggling it if you have to in order to get it all the way home. Make sure it slides all the way down until it rests against the conical-shaped shoulder on the shaft. Also see to it that the key doesn't fall or slide either in or out along its slot; you want the end of the key to be about 1/8 inch below (or in) from flush with the top (or outer) surface of the flywheel, so it'll wind up flush when you cinch the flywheel down.

Put the washer on the shaft over the flywheel. If the washer is cupped, put the cupped side toward the flywheel, so that the outer edges of the washer are the first part to touch the wheel. Spin the big flywheel nut onto the engine shaft (cl in most cases, but c-cl if the nut came off cl) if the wheel is held on by one. Those of you who have a Briggs and Stratton engine with a starter clutch that's supposed to spin on, make sure the clutch still slips easily over the end of the engine shaft. Sometimes the end of the shaft gets widened out when you hammer down on it to loosen the flywheel. If your starter clutch catches at all on the drive shaft, take the clutch off and file all around the end of the shaft until the clutch will fit over it easily. Then spin the clutch on (cl).

Tighten (cl on most models) the flywheel nut to 30 foot-pounds on Tecumseh engines, and to at least 50 foot-pounds on Briggs and Stratton engines. If you are tapping on (cl) a Briggs and Stratton clutch, tap until the clutch simply won't turn any farther.

Check and/or adjust the "air gap," the narrow space between the ends of the armature and the flywheel (see illustration 49—on models like the Tecumseh in illustration 57a, you can't get in there to adjust the gap). Put four 3½ inch strips of Scotch Tape in layers over the shiny magnets on the flywheel rim. Make sure the layers are all smooth, so they will add up to about .008 inch (each piece of tape is about .002 inch thick). Then see if your homemade gauge of Scotch Tape will fit under the armature. It should just slip through. If the gap is too large or too small, turn the flywheel so the magnets are away from the armature. Then loosen (c-cl) the two hex-head screws that hold the armature in place about two turns. Slide the armature as far away from the flywheel as it will go, then tighten (cl) one of the screws. Turn the flywheel until the tape-covered magnets are right under the two armature arms. Loosen (c-cl) the screw, and the magnets will pull the armature down snug against the four layers of tape. Tighten both hex-head screws so it will stay put, then turn the flywheel so you can take the tape off.

Put the blower housing and starter back on the engine, making sure the housing overlaps any other metal shields around the engine. On Briggs and Stratton engines with starter clutches, turn the squarish post in the middle of the starter until the corner with "Top" written on it is pointing to the spark plug as in illustration 49.

The screws that hold the housing to the engine must all be tightened (cl) thoroughly. On Tecumseh engines, the three bolts that go through the blower housing into the head (the part of the engine that the spark plug is screwed into) must be torqued to about 14 foot-pounds.

Screw the spark plug (a nice new one, preferably, to make your whole ignition system first rate) back in (cl) if you took it out, and tighten (cl) it good and tight, to 20 foot-pounds if you want to be exact.

Use the test plug to try out the ignition system. If you get a good blue-white spark, pat yourself on the back, hook up the regular plug, and you're all set. If you still don't get any spark, first read over the whole procedure again and try to think of anything you might have missed. If you did all you could, and you still can't get fire, the generator unit or the condenser may be shot; you have to take the mower to a shop for those major repairs.

Fuel-Air System

Description, General

The fuel-air system delivers a mist of gas and air to the cylinder. The mist has to be made up of 14 units of air to each unit of gasoline by weight. If the mixture goes up to 17 to 1, or goes down to 8 to 1, the engine won't work. That's not much leeway. So the parts of the system, the air cleaner, the fuel line, and the carburetor, must all be in good shape. If you have any troubles with the system as a whole, always start your repairs by *Cleaning the Air Cleaner* (page 210). Then do a *Fuel Line Clean-Out* (page 216) before fiddling with the carburetor. Nine times out of ten you can get the engine working if you do the simple jobs of cleaning out the air and fuel supplies. Then it'll be easier to solve any problem with that complicated gismo, the carburetor, and its control linkage.

Air Cleaner

Description

The air cleaner is the thing sticking up off the carburetor. It may be any of the three types in illustration 58. Its job is simply to clean the air going into the engine, so no dust gets in there and starts wearing down all the moving parts.

Problems

CLEANER CLOGGED

The engine is hard to start, and often makes a chugging, puffing sound when it's running, throwing out clouds of black smoke at the same time. At least part of the problem is likely to be dirt and greasy gunk clogging up the air cleaner. It's time to

CLEAN AIR CLEANER

The cleaning process for each type of air cleaner is different. Find the paragraph below that applies to your cleaner.

To clean *Foam Element Cleaners* (see illustration 58a), unsnap the cap or unscrew (c-cl) the screw that holds the cap down, and take it off (on some models, the whole cleaner comes off the carb—be careful not to let dirt get down into the throat of the carburetor at any time). Pull the cap off the cleaner, then pull the sponge element out. Take a look at the part of the element that was exposed to incoming air. Often that part of the element gets so dirty that no air passes any farther into the system. Brush off accumulations of gunk with a parts brush. Then saturate the whole sponge with kerosene or a liquid detergent that'll cut oil, and squish it around in your hands to work out the dirt. Several soakings and squeezings may be necessary to get the thing clean. When you're satisfied that the gunk in the sponge has been taken out by the solvent, wrap a dry rag around the element and wring out all the liquid. Pour about two table-spoons of oil (the same oil you use in the engine) onto the dry sponge and work it around in your hands again until the oil is evenly distributed. Give the sponge a good

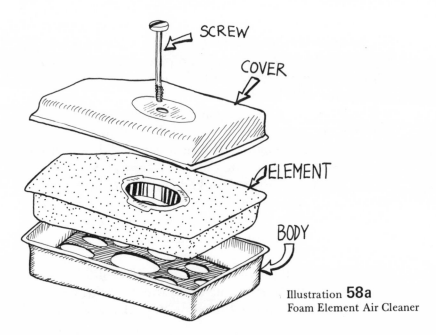

Illustration **58a**
Foam Element Air Cleaner

211

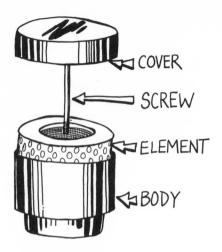

COVER

SCREW

ELEMENT

BODY

Illustration **58b**
Oil Bath Air Cleaner

GASKET

final squish to let any extra oil drip off. Wipe off the inside of the body and cap of the air cleaner with a rag. Replace the foam element in the body. If the element has a lip around it, make sure this lip sticks out over the edge of the cleaner body, so when you put the cap on, the whole thing will seal together evenly. Check the gasket that goes between the cleaner and the carburetor; if it's broken, replace it, and if it's dirty, clean it off. Put the cap on, snapping it well into place if it's the snap-on type. If there is a screw for holding the air cleaner to the carburetor, check it for straightness; take the screw and roll it along the edge of something very flat, like a formica counter, with the head just hanging over the corner. As the screw rolls along, see if it bows up and down. A good straight screw (a rare thing in any interpretation) will roll evenly. If your screw is crooked (far, far too many are), get an exact replacement—straightening rarely works. Tighten (cl) the screw thoroughly but not so much that the soft aluminum threads of the carburetor get stripped.

Cleaning an *Oil Bath Air Cleaner* (see illustration 58b) starts with unscrewing (c-cl) the wing nut on top of the cleaner. Sometimes the whole top of the air cleaner

unscrews (c-cl) instead of just a wing nut. When the nut
or top is off, spread a rag out on a flat surface, then lift
the whole cleaner off the carburetor and set it down right
side up on the rag. Pull the element out of the body of
the cleaner and look for dirt and sludge on the bottom
of the element and settled to the bottom of the oil reservoir in the bottom of the cleaner body. Soak the element
in kerosene or some other solvent, dump the old oil out
of the body, and wipe out the settled dirt with a rag, if
the system is dirty. Fill the body to just below the "Fill"
level. Check the gasket that goes between the cleaner and
the carburetor. If it's dirty, clean it off. If it's broken or
all squished out of shape and cracked so it doesn't seal
things up, replace it. Dirty air leaking into the carburetor
can deliver nasty dust into the cylinder, where it will wear
down the walls and other things, taking years off the life-
span of the engine. Check the stud (the threaded pole
that the wing nut goes on, or that sticks down from the
cap) for straightness. If it sticks up at an angle, the cleaner
won't seal. Bend the stud with your bare hands, carefully
so you don't break it off. If the stud breaks off, or if the
threads strip out of the carb, you have to have a shop
replace it, or the cap, or the whole carburetor. Put the
element back into the cleaner body, then put the whole
works back on the carburetor and tighten (cl) the wing
nut or the cap thoroughly.

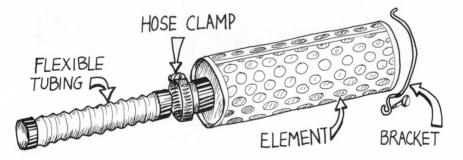

Illustration **58c**
Paper Element Air Cleaner

Cleaning a *Paper Element Air Cleaner* (see illustration 58c) begins with either loosening (c-cl) the screw on the hose clamp as in illustration 58c, or loosening (c-cl) the wing nut that holds the cleaner cover down (this wing nut may be under the cleaner and carb on some models). Some elements can come out of the metal screen cylinders that hold them, but most are sealed in for good. To clean the assembly, simply tap it against a hard surface, turning it around and around so the dust can shake off on all sides. If the paper is hopelessly caked with dust, or greasy and grimy, replace it. No old paper element works as well as a new one. Some filters, for instance those on a few models of Briggs and Stratton engines, are washable, if you use a non-sudsing detergent. But don't wash the element unless you know from your owner's manual that it's OK to do so. If there's any question, just replace the element—it won't cost more than a buck, usually. If there is a gasket between the cleaner and the carburetor, check it for dirt and wear. Clean it if it's dirty, replace it if it's all squished out of shape or cracked with age. Put the cleaner (and its cover if there is one) back in place and tighten (cl) the wing nut or hose clamp screw so the system is sealed tightly again.

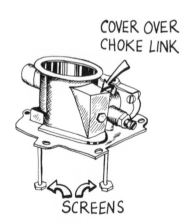

COVER OVER CHOKE LINK

SCREENS

Illustration **59a**
B & S Automatic Choke Carburetor

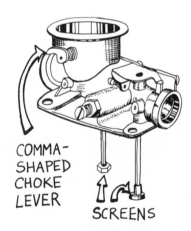

COMMA-SHAPED CHOKE LEVER

SCREENS

Illustration **59b**
B & S Pulsa Jet Carburetor

Fuel Line

Description

The fuel line is made up of the gas tank (you know, silly, the thing you put the gas into) and the tube that carries the gasoline from the tank into the carburetor. On many engines, the carburetor sits right on top of the gas tank, so you can't see the tube because it just sticks right down from the carb to the bottom of the tank (see illustrations 59a, b, c, d, e, 66a, b).

Problems

GRASS-IN-THE-GAS

(Also *water, rust, or dirt* in the gas.) The engine is hard to start, or runs for a while, then quits, and you have done the four quickie tests and narrowed your problem down to the fuel line. On looking into the gas tank, you see leaves of grass floating down there (no, not the book of poems, the real thing), or maybe you see globules of water clustered around the bottom of the tank, with rust appearing on the bottom and sides of the tank. Or maybe, if you have a bowl-type carburetor, you find that water comes burbling out when you push the drain button of the bowl. All of these symptoms call for the same treatment:

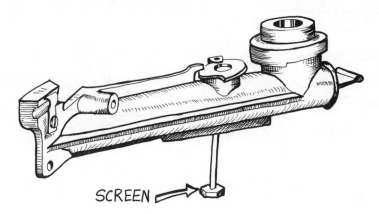

SCREEN

Illustration **59c**
B & S Vacu Jet Carburetor

FUEL LINE CLEAN-OUT

To clean the fuel line, start by emptying the gas tank with a siphon or "Okie Credit Card."

Get a three-foot length of clean plastic tubing from a car parts store (if the store has a hand siphon, you can get one of those for a buck or so; it'll work OK if the valve in it is any good). Practice using the siphon with tasteless water first if you're new to the art of siphoning. Stick one end of the siphon in a bucket of water that you have set up outside on a cinder block or something. Put the other end of the tube in your mouth and grab it near the mouth end with one hand, ready to pinch the tube closed. Suck water half way up the tube, pinch the mouth end closed tightly, then take that end out of your mouth and lay it on the ground. Release your pinch grip on the tube and the water should run out. Do the procedure a few times until you are good at it, then go use the siphon to empty the gas tank. If you think you just have a minor grass-in-the-gas problem, you can fill the tank with clean gas, siphon it off again (taking any grass out with the siphon as if it were a vacuum cleaner), then fill her up with fresh clean gas a third time and see if she goes. But if the tank is really a rusty filthy mess, you

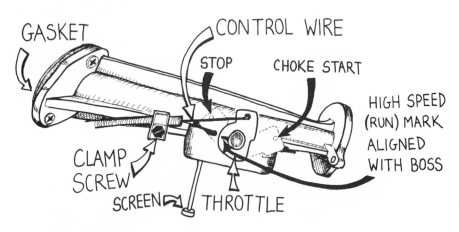

Illustration **59d**
Craftsman Tank Mounted Carburetor

216

have to do more; follow each of the *Tank Removal, Tank Clean-Out, Fuel Pipe Clean-Out,* and *Tank Reassembly* procedures that apply to your carburetor setup.

TANK REMOVAL

To take most *Tecumseh* tanks off, all you have to do is slide it up out of its metal brackets, then pull off the rubber fuel hose from the bottom of the tank, and the air cleaner if it's down there too, and the tank is ready for the *Tank Clean-Out.*

On a few Tecumseh engines, however, the tank is built into the blower housing. Unscrew (c-cl) the housing screws, and take the whole thing off, undoing the fuel line as you do so.

On some *Briggs and Stratton* engines, and some other brand engines, the job is simple also, except that the tank is often held to the engine by bolted straps which must be undone (c-cl). The rubber fuel hose is sometimes held to the tank outlet by a wire spring, the ends of which must be squeezed together to let the tank outlet loose. When you have any of these tank types off, go to the *Tank Clean-Out* paragraph below.

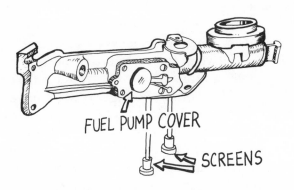

FUEL PUMP COVER

SCREENS

Illustration **59e**
B & S Big Engine Pulsa Jet Carburetor

On most newer and older *Briggs and Stratton* engines, and on some *Craftsman* engines, however, the process of taking the gas tank off is more difficult. It involves removing the carburetor and the gas tank as a unit. Don't let that throw you; it's still not a big project. First figure out which carburetor setup you have by looking at illustration 59, then go to the paragraphs for your carburetor below.

To remove *Briggs and Stratton* Vacu jet and Big Engine Pulsa jet carburetor units, and *Craftsman* tank-mounted fuel systems, first undo the throttle control wire if there is one; unscrew (c-cl) the screw that clamps the housing for the wire, take the housing out of the clamp altogether, then take a felt pen and mark the hole on the throttle that the wire goes into with an "O," and work the wire around so its Z-shaped end pulls out of the hole. See if there is a stop switch as on the Briggs and Stratton unit in illustration 60. If there is, undo the wire by pushing the blade in as shown, or by unscrewing (c-cl) the little screw that holds it. Take the air cleaner off your Briggs and Stratton carb now, too, and undo one end of the spring (see illustration 60) by using needlenose pliers and much care so you don't bend or stretch it out of shape.

Next look at the gasket that's between the carburetor and the engine (see illustration 59d). If the gasket looks cracked or misshapen or decayed so that it isn't sealing the joint between the carburetor and the engine, make a note to get a replacement before your reassemble the unit. Unscrew (c-cl) the two big screws that hold the carburetor to the engine, each a bit at a time, so the whole outfit comes loose evenly. Put the screws in a dixie cup so you can't lose them, then jiggle and pull the carb until it detaches from the gasket. Pull the tank and carburetor unit down and away from the engine an inch or so. On Craftsman engines the thing will now be free to come all the way off. On Briggs and Stratton engines, like in illustration 60, the governor link will still be hanging you up. Hold the carb and tank with one hand and work them around gently, tipping and turning at different angles as you hold the link with the other hand and get the Z shape in the end of the link to slide out of the hole in the throttle. Mark that hole with an "X" so you'll know which one it is later.

Carburetor and gas tank clear of the engine now? Good. It wasn't too much of a hassle, was it? It just looks kind of weird to see the engine all naked. Clean off the outside of the carb and the tank meticulously with a rag so you won't get any grime in the works when you open things up. Find the screws that hold the tank to the base of the carburetor, and unscrew (c-cl) them, each one just a bit at a time, working your way around and around the carb instead of loosening one screw all the way at once, which might mess up the gasket or warp the joining surface of the carb and the tank. Keep all the screws in a dixie cup so you don't lose them.

Pull the carburetor away from the tank gently, trying not to mess up the gasket too much. If the gasket does get ruined, make a note to get a new one. Be careful also as you draw the fuel pipe(s) up out of the hole(s) in the tank; you don't want to catch the screen that's

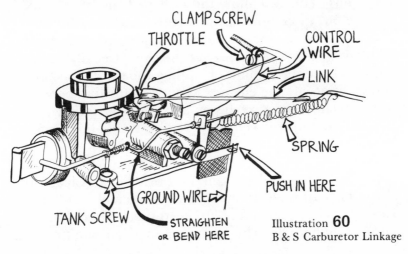

CLAMP SCREW
THROTTLE
CONTROL WIRE
LINK
SPRING
PUSH IN HERE
GROUND WIRE
TANK SCREW
STRAIGHTEN or BEND HERE

Illustration **60**
B & S Carburetor Linkage

219

mounted on the end of the pipe and break it off. Put the carburetor on a nice clean rag, promise to *keep* the carb clean, and you're ready to go down to the *Tank Clean-Out* below.

To remove *Briggs and Stratton* Pulsa jet and Automatic Choke tank and carburetor units, start by putting the throttle control in the stop position and removing the air cleaner.

On automatic choke models, do a quick test to see if that automatic choke is working before you go any further; leave the throttle at the Stop position and the air cleaner off, but turn the air cleaner screw back into (cl) its hole a few turns. Then give the starter several full, brisk pulls; if the choke plate is closed when the engine is at rest, and turns partly open for a second toward the end of each pull, then closes again, your choke is OK. If the plate doesn't work that way, do the repairs indicated as you come to them in the procedure below.

Loosen (c-cl) and remove the two mounting bolts shown in illustration 61. Then pull the tank and carburetor unit about an inch straight out from the engine, just far enough to undo it from the intake tube and (in many cases) the breather tube. The link will pivot out, but it will still hang you up, so twist the unit as in illustration 61. This will allow the Z-shaped end of the link to slide out of its hole in the throttle on the carburetor. It may take some jockeying and wiggling around of the carb and gas tank unit, but get the thing free of the link without bending the link or ripping the whole link and spring gismo off the engine. As soon as the link comes out of its hole, take a felt pen and mark the hole with a big "X" so you will know where to put that link back in later.

Carburetor and gas tank unit off? Great. Clean off the outside of the carb and the tank assembly with a solvent-soaked rag, and try to keep them meticulously clean from here on. The next step on an automatic choke

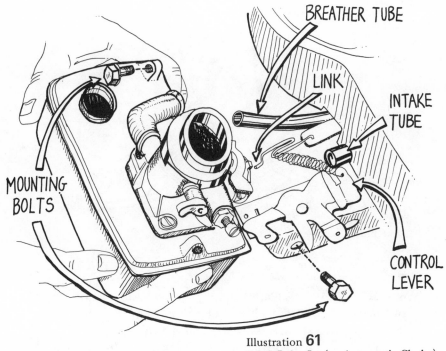

BREATHER TUBE

LINK

INTAKE TUBE

MOUNTING BOLTS

CONTROL LEVER

Illustration **61**
B & S Pulsa Jet (or Automatic Choke)
Carburetor Removal

carburetor is undoing (c-cl) the small hex-head screw
that holds the cover over the choke link (see illustration
59a). Pop the cover off, using a screwdriver under the
skirt at the bottom of the cover if necessary, and put the
cover, its gasket, and the small hex-head screw in a safe
place. Pull the link end out of the offset shaft for the
choke plate as in illustration 62.

On all setups, the next step is loosening (c-cl) all
the screws that hold the carburetor. Loosen (c-cl) each
screw only a big (like 1/8 turn) at a time to start with,
and move from screw to screw in the order shown in
illustration 63. If you have less screws than five, do the
same sort of loosening pattern, going from screw to screw
diagonally across the carburetor base as much as possible.
This will prevent messing up the thin diaphragm and
warping either the carburetor or the gas tank where the

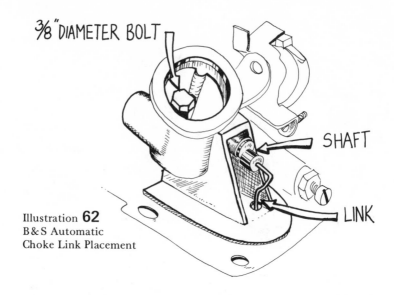

⅜″ DIAMETER BOLT

SHAFT

LINK

Illustration **62**
B & S Automatic
Choke Link Placement

two fit together. Once all the screws are loose, you can take them all the way out (c-cl). Put them in a dixie cup, along with their washers, if they have them.

Pull the carburetor and the gas tank apart gently. You can tap the carb lightly to jar it loose, but *don't* pry under the carb with a screwdriver—it's all too easy to ruin the sealing surfaces. Draw the carburetor up off the tank slowly, making sure you don't damage the little screen ends on the fuel pipes (or the choke link on the automatic choke models). Put the carb down on a very clean rag. Take the diaphragm of the top of the tank (the choke link and spring will come along too on the automatic choke jobs), and put it on the clean rag with the carburetor. You're finally set to go on to

TANK CLEAN-OUT
Get a carburetor cleaning solvent like Gum Out or something similar. Pour about a half cup of the solvent into the empty gas tank. If there is rust in a metal tank, or a build-up of reddish-brown gummy residue because you left gas in the tank for more than a month at a time, get a handful of gravel (the kind with sharp little rocks, called

"pea gravel") and throw it in with the solvent. Let the solvent sit in a metal tank for at least two hours, but *don't* let the solvent sit for more than a half hour in a plastic tank, if that long. Shake the gravel around in the tank if there was rust or gum. Alternate periods of shaking the gravel and letting the thing soak, until you have all the gunk out of the tank. If you can't get all the rust out, take the tank and model number of the engine to a shop and get a new tank. Don't forget to buy gaskets, if any were ruined.

FUEL PIPE (OR TUBE) CLEAN-OUT
Look at the end of the pipe(s) or tube that went into the gas tank. If there is rust or brown gummy reside all around it, the tube or pipe needs to be cleaned or replaced.

On *Tecumseh* and many other engines, it's a snap to just pull off the fuel tube from the inlet into the carburetor, and replace it with a new tube that's the same diameter and length. Before you put the new tube in, though, check for gum and grit in the carburetor inlet. Clean it out with a Q-tip soaked in solvent, then you can push the new tube firmly into place.

On *Briggs and Stratton* and *Craftsman* engines with tank-mounted carburetors, look for the reddish brown gum residue around and in the screen (see illustrations

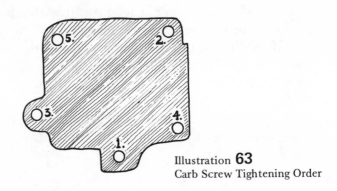

Illustration **63**
Carb Screw Tightening Order

223

59a, b, c, d, e). If a white nylon pipe and screen have gunk in them, just unscrew (c-cl) the gunky old thing, using a socket on the hex-shaped screen holder, and take it and the model number of the engine to a good mower engine shop to get an exact replacement, one that's the same size and length. Don't forget to buy replacements for any of the gaskets that you found ruined during tank removal. Screw in (cl) the new pipe carefully, making sure that you don't over-tighten (cl) it. If you have a gunky brass pipe and screen, don't try to replace it. Put some solvent in a glass or metal tumbler, and stick the pipe down into the solvent. Let the gunk soak off for a few hours, but make sure the solvent doesn't get up into the carb during this soaking. The rubber or plastic parts in the carburetor will disintegrate if the solvent gets on them. Clean the solvent off the pipes, then blow through them to see if they are clogged, or cleared out. If no amount of soaking with solvent will clear the pipe, take the whole carb to a shop for a complete overhaul. Get any gaskets you need to put the fuel system back together while you're at it.

TANK REASSEMBLY

The first step in tank reassembly is putting the gas cap back on the tank. But take a critical look at the cap. Bent? Rusty? Grungy? If it's bent, straighten it out or get a new one. If it's rusty or covered with grime, clean it with solvent and the parts brush. Make sure that the tiny hole for air is open. Clean it out with a pin or with an awl or icepick, then blow through it. If there is a round cardboard disc in the cap, make sure that air can pass through the pinholes in the cardboard, too. Put your new or refurbished gas cap on (cl) the cleaned-out tank.

Then promise yourself that you won't ever leave the mower out in the elements again so the tank and gas cap can get rusty.

To reassemble *Tecumseh* tanks, as well as those on some old *Briggs and Stratton* and other engines, all you have to do is push the tank outlet into the end of the fuel tube and slip the tank onto its mounting brackets. If the mounting brackets have screws, tighten (cl) the screws well.

To reassemble *Briggs and Stratton* Vacu jet and big engine Pulsa jet, as well as *Craftsman* tank-mounted carburetor systems (see illustration 59c, d, e), the first step is to make sure you have all the gaskets you need and all the sealing surfaces clean and free of old pieces of gasket. Scrape and wire-brush the old gasket pieces off the surfaces, being careful not to gouge or dent those smooth metal surfaces.

Check the surface of the tank which the gasket fits onto for flatness. Move a metal straightedge (like a ruler) across the surface, and see if there is any space under it. The space will destroy the suction that makes the carb work. If the tank is dented or bent, or if there is unevenness for any reason in the joining surface, replace the tank.

On Briggs and Stratton big engine Pulsa jet carburetors, take off the pump cover by loosening (c-cl) the screws a bit at a time, in staggered order (see illustration 63). Blow through the tubes in the cover and clean them out with toothpicks if they need it. Inspect the diaphragm minutely for holes or torn places. Check the spring to make sure it can push in and out freely. If the spring is sticky or rusty, or if the diaphragm is shot, get exact replacements by taking the old parts and the engine model number to the mower engine shop. Reassemble the parts as shown in illustration 64. Tighten (cl) the screws by bits at a time, in the same order you loosened them. That way the diaphragm won't get pulled out of shape, and the joining surfaces won't get warped.

On all systems in this category, fit the nice new or undamaged gasket in place between the carb and the tank, and screw the mounting screws in (cl), alternating between the screws and tightening just a bit at a time to draw the two parts together evenly, making a tight seal on the gasket.

Take the whole tank and carb unit in one hand, and move it up to the engine. On *Briggs and Stratton* engines, twist and work the unit around and use your free hand to hook the governor link into the "X" hole in the throttle plate (see illustration 60). Then put the gasket on the engine, making sure the thing is on straight so the holes all match up. Screw in (cl) the carburetor screws a bit at a time, alternating back and forth, as always, to make a tight, even seal on the gasket.

Carb on right? Great. On *Briggs and Stratton* engines, hook up the spring, and the stop wire if you have one, as shown in illustration 60. On all engines with remove controls, check the control wire for bends, and straighten out any you find with pliers. Put the control lever in the position that pulls the unattached end of the wire as far as possible into the housing. Then hook the Z at that end into its hole in the throttle, the hole you marked "O" with a felt pen before you took the wire out. Put the housing back into position under the clamp, loosening (c-cl) the clamp screw if necessary, then pull the housing toward the control lever so that the throttle is pulled all the way to the extreme nearest the housing clamp. Tighten (cl) the clamp screw, and try the remote control out without starting the engine, watching to see that the wire moves the throttle from one extreme to the other, opening and closing the choke if there is a "Choke" position on the remote control lever. Problems? See *Throttle Control Adjustment*, page 233. If the control wire is working, put the air cleaner back on, check the cleaner mounting screw for straightness, and the gasket for a good, smooth, undamaged sealing surface. Replace either if questionable. Fill the tank with fresh clean gas, and you're set to go.

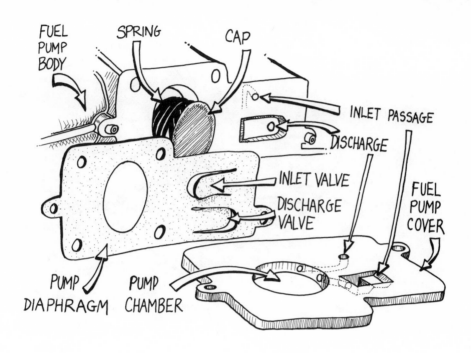

Illustration **64**
B & S Big Engine Pulsa Jet Carb Parts

To reassemble *Briggs and Stratton* Pulsa jet and Automatic Choke models, first take a critical look at the diaphragm. If there are any holes, tears, or worn-off places, replace the thing. On the automatic choke models, check for a squished, bent, or stretched choke link and spring. They both have to be very precise, so replace them if there is any question at all, especially if the choke didn't pass the quick test you gave it at the start of the *Tank Removal* procedure. Push the new spring gently into place over the short tip of the link. Then position the diaphragm and link as in illustration 65.

On all models, make sure the diaphragm is on right so that the screw holes all show. Then put the spring and its cup on *top* of the diaphragm as in illustration 65, and ease the carburetor down into place.

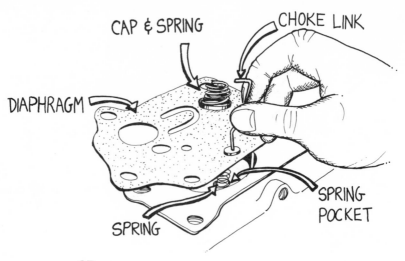

CAP & SPRING

CHOKE LINK

DIAPHRAGM

SPRING POCKET

SPRING

Illustration **65**
B&S Automatic Choke
Parts Placement

On the automatic choke models, check for free motion of the offset shaft (illustration 62—to clean a sticky choke shaft, hold the choke plate open with your fingers, pull out the shaft, clean it off and put it back), then plug the end of the link back into its hole, and replace the cover gasket, cover, and screw (cl).

On all models, start (cl) the screws into their threads. On the models other than the automatic choke ones, tighten (cl) the screws up a bit at a time, in staggered sequence as in illustration 63.

As for you automatic chokers. Get a 3/8 inch diameter bolt that's at least 3 inches long from the hardware store, and stick it straight down the side of the carburetor throat that is normally farthese from the engine (see illustration 62). This will open the choke plate all the way, and then some, thus loading up the spring down under the diaphragm. When you have the spring loaded that way, tighten (cl) the screws that hold the carb to the tank a bit at a time, in staggered sequence as in illustration 63.

When the carb and tank unit is together on all models, put the whole thing in the position shown in illustration 61. Put the Z end of the link into its hole in the throttle plate, the hole you marked before. Then push the carb onto the intake tube, and slide the rubber sleeve over the breather tube. Screw the mounting bolts in (cl) tightly. On automatic choke models, do the same check you did at the beginning of the *Tank Removal* (page 220), just to make sure the choke is AOK.

If the carburetor had a remote control wire hooked up to it, set the control lever in the "Fast" position. Then hook the Z at the carb end of the wire into the hole at the end of the lever that has the mark you made on it. Now turn the whole throttle plate clockwise until it either stops (on automatic choke carbs) or until its curved arm just touches the comma-shaped or reverse L shaped choke lever (see illustration 59b). Hold the throttle in that position, slip the wire housing under the clamp, and tighten (cl) the clamp screw so it holds the housing firmly. Replace the air cleaner, check the screw that holds it for straightness, then screw it in (cl). Finally, fill your nice clean tank up with fresh clean gas, and you're all set to go.

Carburetor

Description
The complicated little bugger that mixes the fuel and air and sends them on into the cylinder. Carbs consist of a throat and some kind of a mixing valve (very often a needle valve or a couple of needle valves). Sometimes a bowl helps keep the fuel supply even, sometimes a diaphragm does the same thing; on some models, a primer improves the supply for starting (see illustration 66a, b). There are eight zillion different variations on the theme, as well as another eight zillion types of control gismos. I can't cover them all. Read about the one I cover that's closest to yours, then use your owner's manual to learn the idiosyncrasies on the model you have. Don't hesitate

to throw up your hands in despair and take a carburetor
that stumps you to a pro. I've had to do that many times.

Problems

TOO RICH OR TOO LEAN

You've fixed everything else on the engine in an effort to
avoid having to tinker with the goddam carb, but you've
been forced to admit that the carb is out of adjustment
or gunked up. Or else some other procedure sent you here
as a last resort. Or maybe your spark plug told you that
you are running the engine too rich or too lean. Whatever
the reason, you have to do a little

CARBURETOR ADJUSTMENT

First figure out which parts, if any, are adjustable on
your carburetor. Some carbs don't have any adjustments.
But if you see the heads of screws sticking out a half inch
or so from the body or bottom of the bowl of the carburetor, with springs under the heads, these are probably
adjustable needle valves. See if you can see the tips of
these screws without taking them out. If the screw goes
through a plate and the tip is visible on the other side, it
will be a speed screw, not an adjustable needle valve.
Ignore the speed screws for the moment; they're covered
below. Just find the needle valve(s).

To *Adjust Needle Valves,* first fill the gas tank half
full so you're sure you're getting a steady fuel supply.
Then find out what the initial adjustment should be for
your particular carburetor. It will be a number like 1½
turns open. That's what it is for almost all *Briggs and
Stratton* engines. But find what it is for your own, then
remember it. To set a screw at its initial setting, turn it
clockwise *gently* until it *just barely* snugs against the hole
it screws into. *Do not* tighten (cl) the screw firmly. If
you tighten the thing too hard, it'll ruin itself and the
hole it goes into as well. When the screw is just snug, look
at the position of the screwdriver slot (is it horizontal,

vertical or diagonal?), then loosen (c-cl) the screw the right number of turns, like 1½ on most *Briggs and Stratton* engines. Keep in mind that as you turn the screw, the slot will pass the horizontal position *twice* for each full revolution. If you have more than one adjustable needle valve, set the others in the same way. Make *sure* you are doing this adjustment right. If you don't have an owner's manual, get one from a parts distributor, or from a shop, or ask them what the initial adjustment should be for the needle valves for your model number engine. *Don't* do the adjustment by guess and by god. God probably doesn't give a hoot.

Start the engine (if it won't start, and you have eliminated all other possible ignition, fuel line, and air cleaner problems, take it to a pro—the carb is very sick inside and needs intensive care) and let it warm up for a few minutes. When it's warm, put the throttle in the Fast position, and find the high-speed needle. If there is only one adjustable needle, that's it. If there are two adjustable needles, the one on the bottom of the bowl will be the high-speed needle, or the one that's *farthest* from the intake to the engine (see illustration 66a, b). In other words, if the two screws are right next to each other, the one closest to the

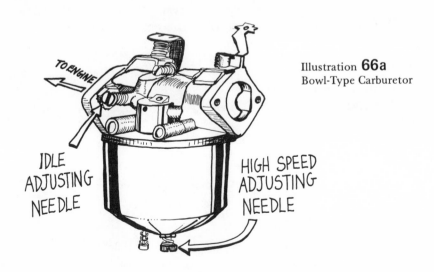

TO ENGINE

IDLE ADJUSTING NEEDLE

HIGH SPEED ADJUSTING NEEDLE

Illustration **66a**
Bowl-Type Carburetor

air cleaner is the high-speed needle. As the engine runs at high speed, look at the position of the screwdriver slot, and memorize it. Then turn the screw clockwise (thus making the mixture leaner) until you hear the engine begin to miss and skip. Quickly, before the engine stops, turn the screw counterclockwise back to its original position. Now turn it counterclockwise more, until the engine begins to strain and puff out black smoke from being too rich. Turn the screw clockwise back toward its lean setting. But don't go quite all the way to the midpoint between the two extremes, only about three-fourths of the distance from the too-rich position to the midpoint. Leave the thing adjusted a little rich, in other words.

To adjust the idle mixture needle, fiddle with the throttle control until the engine is running slowly, but smoothly (around 1700 rpm is what you want, but most of us can't tell what rpm that is by listening). Do the same sort of adjustment on the idle mixture needle as you did on the high-speed one.

SPEED SCREW ADJUSTMENT

After you have done the above adjustments, put the throttle control in the idle position. If the engine idles too slow or too fast, you can now change the idle speed by screwing in the idle speed screw (cl) and out (c-cl). Try to adjust the idle speed so the engine runs slowly

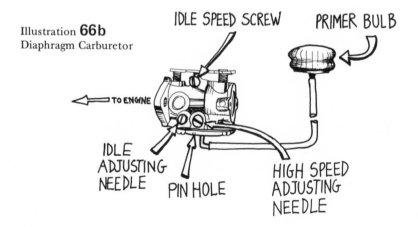

Illustration **66b**
Diaphragm Carburetor

IDLE SPEED SCREW

PRIMER BULB

TO ENGINE

IDLE ADJUSTING NEEDLE

PIN HOLE

HIGH SPEED ADJUSTING NEEDLE

without missing at all. If there are two speed screws, adjust the one that affects the idle only. Leave the high-speed adjusting screw to the pros.

If the carburetor refused to adjust, or if it adjusts itself willfully, or if the engine won't run after you have painstakingly adjusted the carburetor, first make sure there isn't some problem with the other parts (do the four quickie tests), then take the thing to a shop and have the carb attended to by an expert. Do *not* take a bowl type carb apart and start bending the float around, even if some self-styled mechanic says that's a good idea. Leave delicate adjustments like that to the pros.

THROTTLE CONTROL
ADJUSTMENT

Good heavens! There are so many different kinds of throttle control setups! There's no way this book is going to cover all of them. Just look at the picture of your setup in your owner's manual (get an owner's manual for your particular model engine from a parts distributor or a mower shop if you don't have one), and compare it to your control. Check for bent links, stretched or distorted springs, or disconnection of any of these parts. Replace or straighten the links that need it. Replace any spring that is questionable at all. Connect the ground wire firmly if it isn't that way. Test the system out again.

If it has a remote control lever, and still either won't stop or run the engine at full speed, or won't work the choke, look for a messed-up remote control wire (see illustrations 59d, 67). If the wire is bent, straighten it. If the choke link isn't pushing the choke all the way on, straighten the bend in it a bit as shown in illustration 67. If the control wire is too short or too long, loosen (c-cl) the clamp screw and screw and push or pull the housing under the clamp to correct the problem. tighten (cl) the clamp screw well, and try out the system again. If the control wire is broken, go to the *Replacement* section on page 236.

If the control wire is simply not long enough (see illustration 68), loosen (c-cl) the clamp screw enough to take the housing out, then unhook the end of the wire and just cut the Z off. Undo whatever is holding the housing at the control lever end of the wire, and slide the housing down until the end of the wire is back about a foot into the housing. Cut 2 or 3 inches off the end of the housing, slide the wire back out and bend a new Z into the end, just like the old one, with needlenose pliers. Hook the new Z back into its hole in the throttle, then pull the control lever so that tie wire is as far as possible up into the housing. Slip the housing under the clamp screw and draw it toward the control lever so that the throttle is moved all the way to its extreme position. Tighten (cl) the clamp screw. If the system still doesn't work, there might be something wrong with the governor. *Don't* mess with the governor. Make sure that all of its links and springs are OK, and take the thing to a pro if it still doesn't work; he can adjust it so the engine won't either quit or wind up so fast that it blows itself apart.

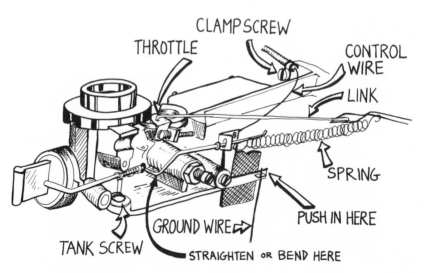

Illustration **67**
B & S Throttle Linkage

234

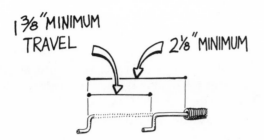

1 3/8" MINIMUM TRAVEL

2 1/8" MINIMUM

Illustration **68**
Throttle Control Wire End

PRIMER WON'T PRIME

The primer, which consists of nothing more than a rubber bulb that can pump a little squirt of extra gas into the carburetor, usually fouls up by coming loose, or by getting stopped up one way or the other.

If the primer makes a nice squishy sound inside the carb when you push it, but the bulb takes a long time to puff back up to its normal unsquished size, the pinhole is probably clogged (see illustration 66b). Clean out the hole with a pin, but don't push the pin more than 1/8 inch into the hole, or you might puncture the diaphragm in there and ruin the whole carburetor.

If the primer bulb squishes down and pops back up to normal size all too easily, without making any squishy squirt in the carb, the tube that connects the bulb with the bottom of the carb is probably undone. Check both ends of it. The carburetor end is easy to hook back up. The bulb end is almost impossible to get at without taking off the blower housing as in the first of the *Breaker Points Overhaul,* page 199.

If the bulb won't even press down, pull the carb end of the tube off its fitting on the bottom of the carb, and clean both the tube and the fitting out with a toothpick. Try the bulb and tube out before hooking them back up, to make sure the line is clear. Still not priming? The problem is probably in the carburetor. Take the whole thing to the shop for a carb overhaul.

THROTTLE CONTROL WIRE
REPLACEMENT

If your control wire is broken or hopelessly bent or twisted, buy about 4 feet of housing, and about 4 feet 6 inches of wire (Bowden Wire, they call it) from the power shop. Attach the lever end of the wire and housing the same way the old ones were attached, then wrap the housing around the mower handle once on the way to the engine so it can't flap around and get tangled in things. Attach the wire and housing to the carburetor as described above in the last paragraph of the *Throttle Control Adjustment.*

THROTTLE CONTROL LEVER
ILLEGIBLE

You have left the mower outside a lot, and the paint markings for the Stop, Slow, Fast, and Choke settings have worn or rusted off. Try starting the mower at each of the two extremes. When it starts, you know it is at the Choke extreme. Mark that extreme with a scratched-on letter C, and mark the other extreme S so you'll always know. Then don't leave the poor old mower out in the rain anymore.

Appendices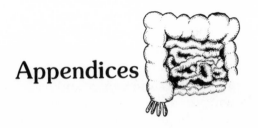

Appendages and How to Keep Them
(Like Toes and Fingers)

1. Clean the lawn before you mow it.
2. Start the engine in a clean, open space. *Never* indoors.
3. Clear all kids and distracting people of the opposite (or same, if you're gay) sex out of the area before you start mowing.
4. *Never* clean or refuel the mower while the engine is running (see Frontispiece).
5. *Never* run the engine without the gas cap and air cleaner in place.
6. Wear heavy pants and boots when mowing.
7. Don't mow steep or wet, slick areas where you might slip under the mower.
8. Mow diagonally across ruts and troughs—that way you won't "bottom out."

Storing Away For Winter

HAND MOWER

1. Oil wheel axles, reel axles, roller shaft, and gears on wheels. If the gears are making funny noises, do the *Wheel Overhaul.*
2. Check the *Cutter Bar Adjustment* with two strips of newspaper.
3. Check the blades for sharpness (see illustration 11).

POWER MOWER

Siphon all the gas out of the gas tank after you've finished your last mow for the season. Then start up the engine and run it until it quits, to make sure there's no gas left at all. If you have a good bowl type carburetor with a drain button (see illustration 66), push the drain button in to make double sure you aren't leaving anything in there to evaporate over the winter and leave an awful coat of brown gum all over the fuel line. While the engine is still warm, undo and ground the spark plug wire, unscrew (c-cl) the oil plug (it'll be square, and under the deck or just under the oil fill hole) and drain the oil out. Replace (cl) the plug and put fresh oil in (see *Prestarting* procedure for hints). Remove (c-cl) the spark plug and put a squirt or two of oil in the cylinder. Crank the engine over a time or two with the starter to spread the oil around, then replace (cl) the plug.

Store the mower in a *clean dry place,* not near any garden fertilizers (fertilizers often put rust-causing fumes into the air).

Spring Checkup

1. Change the engine's spark plug as in *Plug Change.*
2. *Clean the air cleaner!*
3. Fill the gas tank with *fresh,* newly bought gas, and check the gas cap to make sure the little pinhole isn't clogged.
4. Check the oil level. On reel mowers, put a drop of oil on reel axle ends, on the roller shaft, behind the wheels where the gears are, on the chain, and into any oil caps.
5. Check the mounting bolts that hold the engine to the mower to make sure they're tight (cl).
6. Notice the smell of the grass after the first time you mow it. Wouldn't it be better to have the smell unpolluted by the engine smog? Think about converting to a hand mower.

Tools

BASIC SET

Don't try fussing with any mower unless you have these few tools. You should be able to shop around and get a good set for about ten to fifteen bucks.

Crescent Wrench (or adjustable wrench). Get a good one, made of forged steel, with precision-milled jaws. To test how good the thing is, open the jaws just a hair, then see if you can wiggle the lower or movable jaw closer and farther from the fixed jaw. It's OK if the thing can wiggle a little, but it's *not* OK if the lower jaw does not stay parallel with the fixed one as it wiggles up and down. Non-parallel jaws tend to round off bolts and nuts, making them useless. The 6 inch size wrench is adequate, but the 8 inch model will fit bigger bolts and nuts, and give you more leverage, too.

Screwdrivers. Get a wide assortment. Don't try to get by with one or two, or even a set of four that you bought as a package, unless it has
1. A great big screwdriver—over a foot long; low quality is OK.
2. A medium-size screwdriver—¼ inch wide blade; high quality.
3. A stubby screwdriver—the short, wide kind.
4. A small screwdriver—1/8 inch wide blade; high quality helps.
5. Phillips drivers—medium, short, and long.

Parts Brush. One with a nice long handle and stiff, straight wire bristles. When you get it dirty, soak it in solvent, then run the brush over the lip of a garbage can so the gunk sprays off.

Felt Pen. Just the thing for marking parts as you disassemble them, so you'll know how they go back together.

Oil Can. As shown. Fill with motor oil, 20 or 30 weight.

COMBINATION WRENCH

BOX

OPEN END

←COMBO→

SPARK GAPPER

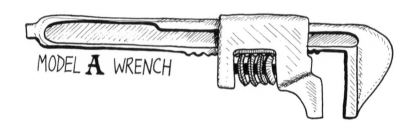

MODEL **A** WRENCH

OIL CAN

WIRE BRUSH

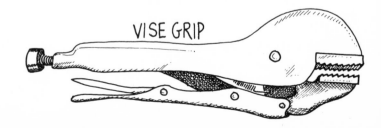

VISE GRIP

Hacksaw. A cheap one will do. Get lots of blades and change them often. A dull hacksaw blade is next to useless.

Solvent. For hand mowers, kerosene or gas will do, but be careful with it. On power mower engine parts, use a carburetor cleaner, like Gum Out, and keep it off your hands.

Additional Tools and Supplies

FOR HAND MOWERS
Emery Cloth. A medium grade is best. Get lots so you don't ever use cloth that's lost its grit.

Valve Grinding Compound. The water soluble kind. It comes in a tube like toothpaste. Car parts stores have it.

FOR POWER MOWERS
These tools run into money. They are listed in order of importance. You should be able to get by with the first five tools, at a cost of about $20, if you shop around and get the cheapest stuff you can. You don't need fancy super-good tools to work on your mower. Very little precision is required of them.

Ratchet and Socket Set. All you need is a functional 3/8 inch ratchet wrench handle, a 2 inch extension, and a cheapo socket set, sizes 3/8 inch to 3/4 inch, and a spark plug socket. Look at flea markets, garage sales, or discount auto parts stores. Some late model engines have small (3/4 inch) spark plugs—for these you have to get the special smaller spark plug socket.

Torque Wrench. One that goes up to 50 foot-pounds or 600 inch-pounds will do just fine. Don't get a fancy heavy-duty one; a decent cheapo will be accurate enough.

Points File. The tiny file that'll fit in tight places. Car parts stores have them.

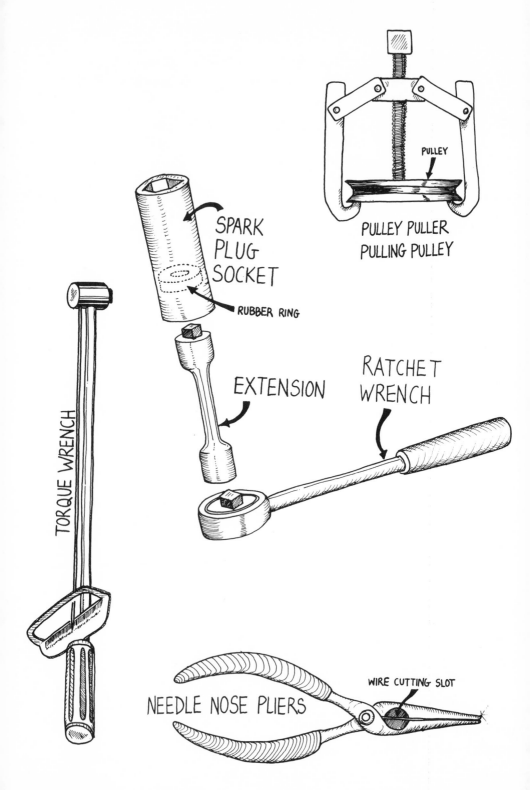

PULLEY

PULLEY PULLER
PULLING PULLEY

SPARK
PLUG
SOCKET

RUBBER RING

EXTENSION

RATCHET
WRENCH

TORQUE WRENCH

WIRE CUTTING SLOT

NEEDLE NOSE PLIERS

Needlenose Pliers. Get a good sturdy pair with jaw tips that line up exactly when you squeeze them together. If they have a wire-cutting slot in the jaws, so much the better.

Sealer. Permatex No. 2 or similar. Don't use it too generously—it'll stick to *anything.*

8x8x8 inch Cinder Blocks. Get at least two from a building supply.

Combination Wrench Set. 3/8 inch to 3/4 inch size range is plenty, and precision isn't important, as long as they are drop forged.

Big Wrench. An old For Model A wrench, or "Knucklebuster" as they are known, will do, but a big (12 inch or larger) crescent wrench is great if you can afford one. For flywheel nuts that are hard to get at, you have to buy a special big socket and use the ratchet.

Channel-Lock Pliers. These are only good if they are well made, so put out a little extra bread (get Craftsman or the real Chann-L-lock).

Vise Grips. Again, the original by that name is best.

Awl or Ice Pick. You know what I mean. Quality ain't important.

Tin Snips. They look like oversized scissors, and they'll cut almost anything. You don't have to get giant ones.

Gear Puller. Hardly worth the cost, considering the small number of times you'll use it.

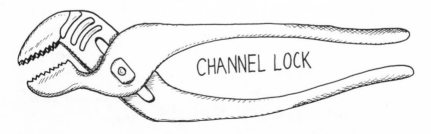

CHANNEL LOCK

Central Parts Distributors
CONTACT THEM FOR YOUR NEAREST SERVICE SHOP

Briggs and Stratton

Birmingham Electric Battery Co.
2230 Second Avenue, South
Birmingham, Alabama 35233

Motor Supply Co.
402-414 N. Central Avenue
Phoenix, Arizona 85004

Motor Supply Co.
33 W. Third Street
Tucson, Arizona 85705

Frank Edwards Co.
1541 Adrain Road
Burlingame, California 94010

Electric Equipment Co.
1611 S. Hope St.
Los Angeles, California 90015

Spitzer Industrial Prod. Co.
43 W. 9th Avenue
Denver, Colorado 80201

Spencer Engine & Magneto, Inc.
1214 W. Cass Street
Tampa, Florida 33601

Auto Electric & Magneto Co., Inc.
800 Lambert Drive, N. E.
Atlanta, Georgia 30324

Mid-States Auto Electric Co.
1905 S. Michigan Ave.
Chicago, Illinois 60616

Magneto Carb. & Elec. Co., Inc.
515 N. 16th St.
Des Moines, Iowa 50314

Central Service & Sales Div.
737 S. 3rd Street
Louisville, Kentucky 40202

Suhren Engine Co.
3000 Dante St.
New Orleans, Louisiana 70150

Chain Battery & Auto Supply, Inc.
Spring at Fannin St.
Shreveport, Louisiana 71101

W. J. Connell Co.
210 Needham Street
Boston, Massachusetts 02164

Auto Electric & Service Corp.
15550 Woodrow Wilson Ave.
Detroit, Michigan 48238

Auto Central Warehouse, Inc.
3100 Joppa Ave.
Minneapolis, Minnesota 55416

Medart Auto Electric Co., Inc.
3134 Washington Blvd.
St. Louis, Missouri 63103

Original Equipment, Inc.
905 Second Ave., North
Billings, Montana 59101

Carl A. Anderson, Inc.
621 S. 16th St.
Omaha, Nebraska 68102

The Durham Co., Inc.
20 Stern Ave.
Springfield, N.J. 07081

Spitzer Electrical Co.
3rd & Mountain Road
Albuquerque, New Mexico 87102

Battery & Starter Co., Inc.
2505 Main Street
Buffalo, New York 14214

F. A. Crossman, Inc.
Tarbell Road
Syracuse, New York 13206

Automotive Electric Assoc., Inc.
306-14 N. Graham Street
Charlotte, North Carolina 28202

Gardner, Inc.
1147 Chesapeake Ave.
Columbus, Ohio 43212

American Electric Ignition Co.
124 N. W. 8th Street
Oklahoma City, Oklahoma 73102

Tracey & Co., Inc.
937 N.W. Glisan St.
Portland, Oregon 97209

Pitt Auto Electric Co.
5135 Baum Blvd.
Pittsburgh, Pennsylvania 15224

R. T. Clapp Co.
2016 Magnolia Ave., N. E.
Knoxville, Tennessee 37917

Automotive Electric Service Co.
982 Linden Ave.
Memphis, Tennessee 38104

Wilson Battery & Electric Co.
618 Jackson St.
Amarillo, Texas 79101

Grayson Company
666 S. Central Expressway
Dallas, Texas 75221

Motor Supply Co.
308 Chihuahua Street
El Paso, Texas 79901

Wahlberg-McCreary, Inc.
2112 Pease Ave.
Houston, Texas 77003

S. X. Callahan
425 N. Flores Street
San Antonio, Texas 78205

Frank Edwards Co.
110 S. Second, W.
Salt Lake City, Utah 84101

Richmond Battery & Ign. Co.
2912 W. Leigh Street
Richmond, Virginia 23230

Bitco Western, Inc.
1741 First Avenue, South
Seattle, Washington 98134

Sunset Electric Co.
N. 703 Division St.
Spokane, Washington 99202

Wisconsin Magneto Co.
4727 N. Teutonia Ave.
Milwaukee, Wisconsin 53209

CANADA

Auto Elec. Serv. (Pacific) Ltd.
1025 Howe Street
Vancouver 1, British Columbia

Auto Elec. Serv. (Western) Ltd.
170 Fort Street
Winnipeg 1, Manitoba

Auto Elec. Serv. Co. Ltd.
1009 Bay Street
Toronto 5, Ontario

Jacobsen

CRAFTSMAN
SEE YOUR NEAREST SEARS RETAIL OR CATALOGUE STORE

Tieco, Inc.
913 North 21st Street
Birmingham, Alabama 35203

Wimberly & Thomas Hardware Co.
1809 First Avenue South
Birmingham, Alabama 35202

Totem Equipment & Supply
322 Concrete Street
P. O. Box 4-912
Anchorage, Alaska 99501

Lawn & Garden Supply
2222 North 27th Street
Phoenix, Arizona 85008

Noble Distributors Inc.
205 South 28th Street
Phoenix, Arizona 85034

Belvedere Sales Company
Route #7 North
Hot Springs, Arkansas 71901

H. V. Carter Company
1305 Divisadero Street
Fresno, California 93721

B. Hayman Company, Inc.
P. O. Box 3847
Terminal Annex
Los Angeles, California 90054

H. V. Carter Company
1700 West 14th Street
Oakland, California 94606

Tarzana Mower & Equipment
Parts, Inc.
6075 Reseda Boulevard
Reseda, California 91335

H. V. Carter Company
2309 Lexington Street
Sacramento, California 95815

Saunders & Company
108 North Sycamore Street
Santa Ana, California 92701

Boyd Distributing Company
1661 West Third Avenue
Denver, Colorado 80223

The Magovern Company
Lawnacre Road
Windsor Locks, Connecticut 06096

De Bra Turf & Equipment
1551 South 30th Avenue
Hollywood, Florida 33020

Clayton-Willard Sales Corp.
1731 Danese Street
Jacksonville, Florida 32206

Tresca Turf Equipment, Inc.
10039 Atlantic Boulevard
Jacksonville, Florida 32211

Charles S. Martin Company
1000 Marietta Street, N. W.
Atlanta, Georgia 30318

Lawn & Turf, Inc.
Interstate 20 at West Avenue
Conyers, Georgia 30207

Craft Center, Limited
517 Ahui Street
Honolulu, Hawaii 96813

Lewers and Cook, Inc.
550 Paiea Street
P. O. Box 9607
Honolulu, Hawaii 96819

Thompson's
1705 Broadway
Boise, Idaho 83706

Power Equipment Company
645 South Route 83
Elmhurst, Illinois 60126

Midwest Turf & Garden Supply
401 South Route 21
P. O. Box 358
Grayslake, Illinois 60030

Illinois Lawn Equipment
14750 South La Grange Road
Orland Park, Illinois 60462

Yeomans Distributors
1503 W. Altorfer
Peoria, Illinois 61614

Steel City Lawn & Garden Eqpt.
155 East 61st Street
Gary, Indiana 46409

Riley's Lawn & Golf Course Eqpt.
6810 Guion Road
Indianapolis, Indiana 46268

Midwest Sales and Service, Inc.
917 South Chapin
South Bend, Indiana 46621

Allied Motor Parts Company
1300 Walnut Street
Des Moines, Iowa 50309

Turf Supply Company
520 Southwest 9th Street
Des Moines, Iowa 50309

Leon Short & Son
918 Main Street
Keokuk, Iowa 52632

Gard'N Wise, Inc.
502 East 33rd Street, N
P. O. Box 4097, North Stn.
Wichita, Kansas 67214

Jack Dayton & Son
743 East Main Street
Louisville, Kentucky 40202

Louisville Cycle & Supply
4800 Allmond Avenue
Louisville, Kentucky 40209

Southern Specialty Sales
617 North Broad Avenue
New Orleans, Louisiana 70119

The Joseph M. Zamoiski Company
1101 De Soto Road
Baltimore, Maryland 21223

G. L. Cornell Company
16031 Industrial Drive
Gaithersburg, Maryland 20760

Center Supply Company
6867 New Hampshire Avenue
Takoma Park, Maryland 20012

R. E. Jarvis Company
371 Boylston Street
Brookline, Massachusetts 02146

Swatelle Brothers
P. O. Box 178
10 Liberty Street
Danvers, Massachusetts 01923

W. F. Miller Company
1593 South Woodward Avenue
Birmingham, Michigan 48011

Ideal Mower Sales
811 Woodward Heights
Ferndale, Michigan 48220

Midwest-Jacobsen
218 South Washington
Lowell, Michigan 49331

Ferguson's
1469 U. S. 31 Shore Drive
Traverse City, Michigan 49684

R. L. Gould & Company
3711 N. Lexington Parkway
St. Paul, Minnesota 55112

Automotive Equipment Company
3117 Holmes
Kansas City, Missouri 64109

Interstate Distributors, Inc.
2015 Grand Avenue
Kansas City, Missouri 64108

Robinson's Inc.
3929 Broadway
Kansas City, Missouri 64111

Twin "C" McCulloch, Inc.
310 Scott Avenue
Kirkwood, Missouri 63122

Outdoor Equipment Company
12012 Manchester Road
St. Louis, Missouri 63131

McGregor Brothers, Inc.
309 North Main
Box 3376 Glenstone Stn.
Springfield, Missouri 65804

A & I Distributors
3517-19 First Avenue South
P. O. Box 1303
Billings, Montana 59103

A & I Distributors
610 East Platinum
P. O. Box 1975
Butte, Montana 59701

A & I Distributors
807 Second Street South
P. O. Box 1187
Great Falls, Montana 59401

Big Bear Equipment Company
12600 West Dodge Road
Omaha, Nebraska 68144

Ziegler Machine Company, Inc.
1515 N. 30th Street
Omaha, Nebraska 68111

Bill Blackwell's Garden Supply
1962 N. Olden Avenue
Trenton, New Jersey 08638

Wilfred MacDonald
3800 Park Avenue
Weehawken, New Jersey 07087

Superior Service Company
4015 Menaul Boulevard
Albuquerque, New Mexico 87110

Wacksman's Lawn & Golf Equip
426 Third Street
Albany, New York 12206

Crest-Jacobsen, Inc.
6245 Fly Road
East Syracuse, New York 13057

Malvese Mower & Equipment
530 Old Country Road
Hicksville, New York 11803

Ronconi Equipment Company
615 Fifth Avenue
Larchmont, New York 10538

Grassland Equipment & Irrig.
892 Troy-Schenectady Road
Lathom, New York 12110

Howard J. Premo
South Racquette Street
Massena, New York 13662

Hoff Brothers
80 Rockwood Street
Rochester, New York 14610

Grass Cutting Equipment
Thruway Park Drive
West Henrietta, New York 14586

Joe L. Pleasants, Inc.
1023 West Morehead Avenue
P. O. Box 1546
Charlotte, North Carolina 28208

McCracken Supply Company
1500 Old Garner Road
Raleigh, North Carolina 27610

Porter Brothers, Inc.
1005 East Dixon Boulevard
P. O. Box 591
Shelby, North Carolina 28150

Dakota Hardware Company
212 North Pacific Avenue
P. O. Box 789
Fargo, North Dakota 58102

Lakeshore Equipment & Supply
Main Street
Bloomingburg, Ohio 43106

The Knodel-Tygrett Company
3250 Spring Grove Avenue
Cincinnati, Ohio 45225

Suburban Industries
4900 Lakeside Avenue
Cleveland, Ohio 45231

Jacobsen Power Lawn Mower Co.
3140 West Bailey Road
Cuyahoga Falls, Ohio 43221

Jacobsen Power Lawn Mower Co.
6570 Mayfield Road
Mayfield Heights, Ohio 44124

Tiffin Lawn Equipment
587 S. Washington Street
Tiffin, Ohio 44883

Toledo Turf Equipment Company
5015 Monroe Street
P. O. Box 5617
Toledo, Ohio 43613

Paul Blakeney Company
330 N. E. 38th Street
Oklahoma City, Oklahoma 73105

Empco, Inc.
814 East 1st Place
Tulsa, Oklahoma 74120

Baltz & Son Company
9817 East Burnside Street
Portland, Oregon 97216

Lucky-JT Distributors
4445 N. E. Glisan
Portland, Oregon 97213

Lyle W. Bennett Company
3723 West 12th Street
Box 8126
Erie, Pennsylvania 16505

Lawn & Golf Supply
647 Nutt Road
Phoenixville, Pennsylvania 19460

Conaway-McCulloch
1116 Castel Shannon Boulevard
Pittsburgh, Pennsylvania 15234

Krigger & Company, Inc.
3025 Babcock Boulevard
Pittsburgh, Pennsylvania 15237

George Sebring & Son
1103 North Fifth Street
Stroudsburg, Pennsylvania 18360

Dakota Turf Supply Company
418 West 19th Street
Sioux Falls, South Dakota 57105

Burghardt Radio Supply, Inc.
621—Fourth Street S. E.
Watertown, South Dakota 57201

Graybar Electric Company, Inc.
1474 Lamar Avenue
Memphis, Tennessee 38104

Bob Ladd & Associates
583 Scott Street
P. O. Box 12271,
Binghamton Station
Memphis, Tennessee 38112

McWhorter, Weaver & Co.
179—2nd Avenue
Nashville, Tennessee 37201

Tanksley's Sales & Service
900 South Street
Nashville, Tennessee 37203

Watson Distributing Company
2400 Railroad Avenue
Beaumont, Texas 77701

Colonial Motor Company
3219 Holmes Street
Dallas, Texas 75215

Watson Distributing Company
6335 Southwest Freeway
Houston, Texas 77036

Watson Distributing Company
9111 Broadway
San Antonio, Texas 78217

Boyd Martin Company
1605 Beck Street
Salt Lake City, Utah 84116

Morse Hardware Company
1025 State Street
Bellingham, Washington 98225

Homelite, Inc.
1911—22nd Avenue S.
Seattle, Washington 98144

Northwest Mower
7723—24th Avenue N. W.
Seattle, Washington 98107

Homelite, Inc.
East 3927 Trent
P. O. Box 2563, Terminal Annex
Spokane, Washington 99220

Tryman Distributors
4757 North 125th Street
Butler, Wisconsin 53007

Horst Engineering & Equip Sales
444 North Madison Street
Chilton, Wisconsin 53014

Reinders Brothers
13400 Watertown Plank Road
Elm Grove, Wisconsin 53122

Wisconsin Turf Equipment
1917 West Court Street
Janesville, Wisconsin 53545

H. A. Crane Company
2722 Sheridan Road
Racine, Wisconsin 53403

CANADA

Bow River Equipment
6120—1A Street
Calgary, Alberta, Canada

Bruce Robinson Electric
14840—115th Avenue
Edmonton, Alberta, Canada

Fallis Turf Equipment
581 Number 3 Road
Richmond, B. C. Canada

Consolidated Turf Equipment, Lt
972 Powell Avenue
Winnipeg, Manitoba, Canada

Halifax Seed Company
1887 Granville Street
Halifax, Nova Scotia, Canada

Spramotor, Limited
1099-1105 York Street
P. O. Box 877
London, Ontario, Canada

National Garden Supply of
Canada, Ltd.
1177 Caledonia Road
Toronto, Ontario, Canada

St. Hyacinthe Sports
2625 Boulevard Vanier
St. Hyacinthe, Quebec, Canada

Brandt Machine & Mfg, Ltd.
705 Toronto Street
Regina, Saskatchewan, Canada

Lawn Boy

Birmingham Elec. Bat. Co.
2230 2nd Ave., S.
Birmingham, Alabama

C. C. Jones Battery & Electric
2440 W. McDowell Road
Phoenix, Arizona

Frank Edwards Co.
1541 Adrian Rd., Millsdale Pk.
Burlingame, California

Electric Equipment Co.
1611 S. Hope St.
Los Angeles, California

Central Auto Electric Co.
1171 Lincoln St.
Denver, Colorado

W. J. Connell Co.
85 Airport Rd.
Hartford, Connecticut

Roberts Brothers Co.
6035 Blair Road. N.W.
Washington, D C

Patten Sales Co.
1021 Hogan St.
Jacksonville, Florida

Patten Sales Co.
603 Cass St., Box 2460
Tampa, Florida

Blalock Mach. & Equip.Co.,Inc.
225 Forsyth Street, S.W.
Atlanta, Georgia

Mid-States Auto Electric
1905 S. Michigan Ave.
Chicago, Illinois

Radio Equipment Co.
1500 Stadium Drive
Indianapolis, Indiana

Lally's, Inc.
118 Fourth St.
Des Moines, Iowa

Cowie Electric Co., Inc.
230 S. Topeka
Wichita, Kansas

Suhren Engine Co.
3000 Dante St.
New Orleans, Louisiana

Chain Batt. & Auto Supply
215 Spring St.
Shreveport, Louisiana

W. J. Connell Co.
210 Needham St.
Newton Upper Falls, Mass

Breech Enterprises, Inc.
2100 E. Maple Road
Birmingham, Michigan

Larsen-Olsen Co., Inc.
900 Turner's Crossroad, S.
Minneapolis, Minnesota

Medart Auto Electric Co., Inc.
3134 Washington Blvd.
St. Louis 3, Missouri

Graham & Ross Merc. Co.
524 First Avenue, S.
Great Falls, Montana

Carl A. Anderson, Inc.
621-3 S. 16th St.
Omaha, Nebraska

E. A. Wildermuth, Inc.
1102 Atlantic Ave.
Brooklyn, New York

Baldwin-Hall Co., Inc.
6552 Ridings Road
Syracuse, New York

Automotive Elec. Assoc., Inc.
312 N. Graham
Charlotte, North Carolina

Rott-Keller Supply Co.
1443 Main Ave.
Fargo, North Dakota

Gardner, Inc.
1147 Chesapeake
Columbus, Ohio

J. C. Hamilton Co.
711 E. Third St.
Tulsa, Oklahoma

Tracey & Co., Inc.
937 N.W. Glisan St.
Portland, Oregon

Sullivan Bros.
445 N. 63rd St.
Philadelphia, Pennsylvania

Pitt Auto Elec. Co.
5135 Baum Blvd.
Pittsburgh, Pennsylvania

Locke Auto Elec. Serv.
525 North Dakota Ave.
Sioux Falls, South Dakota

R. T. Clapp Co., Inc.
2016 Magnolia Ave., N.E.
Knoxville, Tennessee

Automotive Electric Corp.
982 Linden Ave.
Memphis, Tennessee

Central Auto Electric Co.
2208 Texas St.
El Paso, Texas

Wahlberg-McCreary, Inc.
2112 Pease Ave.
Houston, Texas

S. X. Callahan Co., Inc.
425 N. Flores St.
San Antonio, Texas

Frank Edwards Co.
110 South Second, West
Salt Lake City, Utah

Richmond Batt. & Ign. Corp.
2912 W. Leigh St.
Richmond, Virginia

Bryant Distributing Co.
1101 N.E. Boat Street
Seattle, Washington

Wisconsin Magneto Co.
4727 N. Teutonia Ave.
Milwaukee, Wisconsin

Pincor

C. C. Jones Battery & Elect.
320 W Jefferson
Phoenix, Arizona 85003

J. F. Dixon Co.
1835 S. Hope St.
Los Angeles, California 90015

Spencer Engine & Magneto, Inc.
1214 West Cass
Tampa, Florida 33606

John E. Connor Co.
30 Asinof Ave.
Chicopee, Massachusetts 01013

Electrical & Magneto Service Co.
1600 Campbell
Kansas City, Missouri 64108

Wollgast Supply Co.
2783 Dunn Road
St. Louis, Missouri 63136

Strauss Bros. Engine and Equip.
399 Dewolfe Place
Hackensack, New Jersey 07601

Carolina Rim & Wheel Co.
321 S. Blount St .
Raleigh, North Carolina 27601

Williams Service & Supply
1411 North Sheridan
Tulsa, Oklahoma 74115

Tracey & Co., Inc.
N.W. 10th & Glisan St.
Portland, Oregon 97209

Sullivan Brothers
445 N. 63rd Street
Philadelphia, Pennsylvania 19151

Master Repair Service
2423 Broadway N.E.
Knoxville, Tennessee 37917

Mapp Caster & Truck Co.
320 N. Sampson St.
Houston, Texas 77003

Bradshaw Auto Parts Co.
359 Pierpont Avenue
Salt Lake City, Utah 85101

Power Tools Sales Co.
E. 7311 Sprague Ave.
Spokane, Washington 99206

Tecumseh

Birmingham Electric Battery
2230 S. Second Ave.
Birmingham, Alabama 35203

Jones Battery & Electric
2440 W. McDowell Road
Phoenix, Arizona 85009

Frank Edwards Co.
1541 Adrian Rd.
Burlingame, California 94010

Electric Equipment Co.
1611 S. Hope St.
Los Angeles, California 90015

Spitzer Ind. Products Co.
43 W. Ninth Ave.
Denver, Colorado 80204

W. J. Connell Co.
85 Airport Rd.
Hartford, Connecticut 06114

Spencer Engine & Magneto, Inc.
1214 W. Cass St.
Tampa, Florida 33606

Auto Electric of Georgia
738 Forest Road
Atlanta, Georgia 30301

Kokua Sales & Supply, Ltd.
829 Queen St.
Honolulu, Hawaii 96813

Industrial Engine & Parts Co.
2345 S. Pulaski Rd.
Chicago, Illinois 60623

Equipment Service Co.
727 N. Illinois
Indianapolis, Indiana 46204

Lally's Inc.
118 Fourth St.
Des Moines, Iowa 50309

Ellingsworth Auto Electric Co.
1003 East Broadway
Louisville, Kentucky 40204

Suhren Engine Company
3000 Dante Street
New Orleans, Louisiana 70118

Chain Battery & Automotive
215 Spring St.
Shreveport, Louisiana 71101

W. J. Connell Co.
210 Needham St.
Boston, Massachusetts 02164

Auto Central Warehouse, Inc.
3100 Joppa Avenue
Minneapolis, Minnesota 55416

Electrical & Magneto Service Co.
1600 Campbell St.
Kansas City, Missouri 64108

Medart Auto Electric
3134 Washington Ave.
St. Louis, Missouri 63103

Original Equipment Co.
905 Second Ave. N.
Billings, Montana 59101

Carl A. Anderson, Inc.
621 S. 16th St.
Omaha, Nebraska 68102

Spitzer Electric Co.
1023 Third Street, N.W.
Albuquerque, New Mexico 87101

E. A. Wildermuth Co., Inc.
1102 Atlantic Avenue
Brooklyn, New York 11238

Battery & Starter Company
2505 Main St.
Buffalo, New York 14214

E. J. Smith & Sons Company
1041 Hawthorne Lane
Charlotte, North Carolina 28205

United Electric Service, Inc.
312 - 1st Ave., N.
Fargo, North Dakota 58102

Gardner, Inc.
1147 Chesapeake Ave.
Columbus, Ohio 43212

Magneto Ignition Co., Inc.
701 West Fifth St.
Tulsa, Oklahoma 74127

Tracey & Co.
937 N.W. Glisan Street
Portland, Oregon 97209

Sullivan Brothers
445 North 63rd St.
Philadelphia, Pennsylvania 19151

Pitt Auto Electric Co.
5135 Baum Blvd.
Pittsburgh, Pennsylvania 15224

Locke Auto Electric Service
320 West 10th St.
Sioux Falls, South Dakota 57102

Tecumseh
continued

Bauer's Auto Parts
674 Walnut
Memphis, Tennessee 38126

Spitzer Auto. & Ind. Prod.
1055 Stock St.
El Paso, Texas 79940

Wahlberg-McCreary, Inc.
2112 Pease Avenue
Houston, Texas 77003

Frank Edwards Co.
110 South Second Street, W.
Salt Lake City, Utah 84107

Richmond Auto Parts Co.
1207 North Boulevard
Richmond, Virginia 23222

Bitco Western, Inc.
1741 First Avenue South
Seattle, Washington 98101

Gill & Wall, Inc.
167 South Lincoln St.
Spokane, Washington 99204

Wisconsin Magneto Co.
918 N. Broadway
Milwaukee, Wisconsin 53202

CANADA

Huttons Limited
131 - 11th Ave., West
Calgary, Alberta

Loveseth Limited
10180 - 105th St.
Edmondton, Alberta

Magneto Sales & Servce
126 Gore Avenue
Vancouver 4, B.C.

Halifax Ignition Ltd.
2760 Robie Street
Halifax, Nova Scotia

Addison Auto Elec., Ltd.
915 Oxford St.
Toronto 18, Ontario

Lambert Electric, Ltd.
114 Avenue "A", North
Saskatoon, Saskatchewan

Index

d

Damn Thing Won't Start
  (Engine) 158
Dead-Man Clutch 80, 102
Diaphragm-Type Carburetor
  150
Dog, Defined 16
Dog-Type Starter Slippage
  175, 177
Doughnut-Shaped Spacers 37
Dull Blades 32, 61, 126, 141

e

Electric Mowers 7, 139—150
Emptying Gas Tank with
  Siphon 122, 216
Engine:
  Lacks Power 167
  Overheats 167, 196
  Shot to Hell 167
  Squeaks 166
  Starts, Then Stops 165
  Surges 166
  Won't Start 158
Extension Cord 141—144

f

Feeler Gauge 204
Fingers, How to Keep Them
  237
Foam Air Cleaner 211
Frayed Extension Cord 142
Friction Shoe Starter Slippage
  175
Fuel-Air System, General 210
Fuel Line 215
  Clean-Out 216, 223

g

Gapping Points 204
Gapping Spark Plug 197

Gasoline Engine 149—236
  Four Quickie Tests 159
  Fuel-Air System 210
  Ignition 194
  Prestarting Preparations 152
  Replacement 168
  Shopping Hints 149
  Starter 168
  Starting 156
  Troubleshooting 158
Gas-Oil Mix (2 Cycle Engine)
  156
Gas Siphon 122, 216
Gas Tank 153, 215
  Clean-Out 222
  Reassembly 225
  Removal 217
Gnashing, Self-Powered Mower
  137
Grass Catcher 13, 53
Grass-in-the-Gas 123, 215

h

Handle:
  Reel-Type Mowers 51
  Rotary Mowers 134
Hand Mower:
  Cutter Bar 22
  Defined 6
  Grass Catcher 13, 53
  Handle 51
  Reel 22
  Roller 42
  Shopping Hints 10
  Wheels 13—22
Hooks, Grass Catcher 53
Housing:
  Blower 154
    Clean-Out 200
  Mower 131
    Clean-Out 133
  Starter 168, 170
    Clean-Out 200
Hubcaps 15, 115, 118—119

r

s

t

v

w

z

FINIS

notes

notes

notes

photographs by Paul Schoelhamer